HOLBEIN AND THE COURT OF HENRY VIII

THE PIERPONT MORGAN LIBRARY
21 APRIL–30 JULY 1983

MADE POSSIBLE BY A GRANT FROM MOBIL CORPORATION

An exhibition of portrait drawings by Hans Holbein the Younger from the Royal Collection, Windsor Castle; printed books, drawings, autograph manuscripts and letters from the collection of The Pierpont Morgan Library, New York; and paintings and miniatures from other public and private collections.

This book, published in 1977 by The Queen's Gallery, Buckingham Palace, is an introduction to the Royal Collection of Holbein drawings, miniatures and paintings, and is not intended to be a catalogue of the present exhibition. Seventy of the drawings in the Royal Collection are on loan to The Pierpont Morgan Library for this exhibition by gracious permission of Her Majesty Queen Elizabeth II.

1 An Unknown Gentleman (No. 38)

HOLBEIN

and the Court of Henry VIII

The Queen's Gallery
Buckingham Palace   *1978–1979*

Times of opening:
Tuesday–Saturday 11 am–5 pm
Sunday 2 pm–5 pm
The exhibition is closed on Monday, but open on Bank Holidays

Designed by Graham Johnson/Lund Humphries
Printed by Lund Humphries, London and Bradford

Foreword

In the preparation of this catalogue the organisers of the exhibition have incurred an unusually large number of debts. The basis of it has been, inevitably, the catalogue of the Holbein drawings in the Royal Library prepared by Sir Karl Parker and published by the Phaidon Press in 1945, and to this we are indebted not only for much of the detail in the individual entries but also for the approach to the study of the drawings over the whole range of subjects involved: the techniques employed, the degree to which the drawings have been retouched and, above all, Holbein's purpose in making them and his peculiar qualities as an artist. Although much work has been done on Holbein in the thirty-three years since the publication of the catalogue Sir Karl's conclusions require remarkably little qualification and his main theses stand unchallenged.

His results can, however, be amplified. Research into Tudor archives has produced much new evidence about Holbein's sitters. In some cases identifications have been challenged or confirmed, while in others details have been discovered which throw light on the interrelationships of the people depicted, in some cases ties of blood or marriage, in others political links, particularly among those connected with the circle of Thomas Cromwell. We are deeply indebted to Miss Susan Foister, who is preparing a thesis on Holbein for the University of London, and has written most of the biographical sections of the catalogue entries and a substantial part of the Introduction, as well as supplying the note on watermarks.

We are also grateful to Stella Mary Newton for writing the note on costume (pp.20–22), and for supplying valuable notes on the dress worn by individual sitters. Mr. David Starkey of the London School of Economics has provided useful biographical details on several sitters. Dr. Lorne Campbell, Miss Margaret Mann Phillips, Professor Hubertus Schulte Herbrüggen and Professor J. B. Trapp kindly enabled us to see in advance and to quote from their article on the Quentin Metsys portrait of Erasmus (No.5 of this exhibition) which appeared in the *Burlington Magazine* in November 1978. In connection with the miniatures Mr. Graham Reynolds allowed us to use material collected for the catalogue which is being prepared of the miniatures in the Royal Collection and Mr. Jim Murrell gave help over questions of technique. Mr. Christopher Norris kindly informed us of the existence of the copies after thirty-two of the Windsor drawings made by George Vertue and Johann Friedrich Müntz which belonged to Horace Walpole and are now at Sudeley Castle. Unfortunately there was no time to carry out a full examination of these copies and we were only able to incorporate in the catalogue a few of the conclusions to be drawn from them, but it is hoped that in due course a full study of them will be made. We should like to express our gratitude to Mrs. Dent-Brocklehurst for allowing the drawings to be brought to Windsor so that they could be studied carefully and compared with the originals.

Finally we must thank Mr. Graham Johnson and Mr. Anthony Sumner of Lund Humphries for the care and skill with which they designed the catalogue and saw it through the press.

Works cited in abbreviated form

Briquet   C. M. Briquet, *Les Filigranes,* reprinted
Amsterdam, 1968.

Ganz, *Drawings*   Paul Ganz, *Les Dessins de Hans Holbein le Jeune,*
Geneva, 1939.

Ganz, *Paintings*   Paul Ganz, *The Paintings of Hans Holbein,*
London, 1950.

Millar   Oliver Millar, *The Tudor, Stuart and Early
Georgian Pictures in the Collection of H.M. The
Queen,* London, 1963.

NPG, *More*   '*The King's Good Servant*', *Sir Thomas More,*
London, National Portrait Gallery, 1977–78.

Panofsky   E. Panofsky, *The Life and Art of Albrecht Dürer,*
Princeton, 1955.

Parker   K. T. Parker, *The Drawings of Hans Holbein in the
Collection of H.M. The King at Windsor Castle,*
London, 1945.

Parthey   Gustav Parthey, *Wenzel Hollar, Beschreibendes
Verzeichnis seiner Kupferstiche,* Berlin, 1853.

Strong, *Henry VIII* R. Strong, *Holbein and Henry VIII,* London, 1967

Strong, NPG   R. Strong, *National Portrait Gallery: Tudor and
Jacobean Portraits,* London, 1969.

'O stranger, if you desire to see pictures
with all the appearance of life,
Look on these which Holbein's hand
has created'

Nicholas Bourbon (1503–after 1550)

Introduction

The drawings, paintings and miniatures by Hans Holbein the Younger shown in the present exhibition constitute perhaps the most remarkable visual record of a royal court in European art. They are the work of one of the greatest portrait painters of all time and they represent most of the types of people associated with the court of King Henry VIII, whether as members of his family, officials, soldiers, politicians, humanists or friends. The portraits include images of those who served the King well though they were often rewarded with ingratitude, as well as of those who treated him with servility in order to further their own careers. There is a portrait of one of his Queens, Jane Seymour, and of his son Prince Edward, later King Edward VI, as a child. The men range from the heroic Sir Thomas More and the saintly John Fisher to the powerful but unscrupulous Richard Rich and the aristocratic poet Henry Howard, Earl of Surrey. The ladies of the court are also present, particularly those who were in waiting on one or other of his Queens. Some display the charm of youth, such as Mary Zouch (No.45), others are shown in formidable middle age, such as Lady Rich (No.76) or Lady Butts (No.69).

The chief absentee is the King himself. Sadly the Royal Collection contains no original portrait of him, whether drawn or painted, by Holbein. The great mural painting by the artist representing the King, his parents (King Henry VII and Elizabeth of York) and his third Queen, Jane Seymour, was destroyed in the fire at Whitehall Palace in 1698 and is now only known from the lifesize fragment of the cartoon in the National Portrait Gallery, and in later copies. In the present exhibition he is represented in seventeenth-century copies from the wall painting (Nos.81 and 82), miniatures (Nos.89, 90 and 91), two sixteenth-century cameos (Nos.95 and 96) and a medallion (No.99); his suit of armour is also included (No.97). In addition King Henry VIII appears as the central figure in Holbein's miniature representing Solomon and the Queen of Sheba (No.88).

Holbein was born in Augsburg in 1497/8. He was the son of a painter, also called Hans, from whom he received his earliest training. By 1515 he had moved from Germany to Basel where he worked as a designer of woodcuts for various publishers, including Johannes Froben (No.4); in addition he painted portraits and religious pictures and worked on decorative schemes for the Town Hall and for the façades of several houses. In Basel Holbein met Erasmus (Nos.5 and 6) and through him came into contact with a group of distinguished Humanists. He is recorded in Lucerne in 1517 and 1519, and probably travelled to Italy around this time. In 1524 he paid a brief visit to France and then in 1526, because of the religious troubles in Basel, he set off for the Low Countries, stopping at Antwerp, where he met Quentin Metsys (No.5). From there Holbein went on to England and by December he had arrived in London carrying letters of introduction from Erasmus to Sir Thomas More (Nos.1 and 2) and perhaps also to Archbishop Warham (No.14); the latter had received a portrait of Erasmus by Holbein two years earlier. His major work during this first visit was the portrait group of More and his family, now lost, the drawings for which are shown in this exhibition (Nos.1–3 and 7–11), but he also executed single portraits of More and Warham (No.14), as well as of Sir Henry Guildford (Nos.12 and 13). All three of these men were eminent correspondents of Erasmus. During this visit Holbein did not, apparently, establish contact with the court itself, although there are payments in 1527 to a 'Master Hans' (see entry for Nos.12 and 13), and in 1528 he returned to Basel. However these were the years during which the Reformation reached Basel in full force and the city was the scene of dreadful violence and iconoclasm. Many of the religious works which Holbein had painted during his first period in the city were destroyed, and after a stay of four years he returned to London, where he remained almost continuously until his death of the plague in 1543.

On this second visit Holbein was initially employed by several of his fellow-countrymen resident in London who were merchants and members of the German Steelyard; this was the London agency of the Hanseatic League. These included Hans of Antwerp (No.22) and Derich Born (No.25), who were portrayed by Holbein in 1532 and 1533 respectively. Soon afterwards Holbein was taken up by the court and embarked on the most successful phase of his career, as portrait painter to the King and his entourage. In addition to the King himself, Holbein painted

Queen Jane Seymour (Kunsthistorisches Museum, Vienna; Ganz, *Paintings,* No.97, pl.138; see No.46) and the infant Prince of Wales (National Gallery, Washington; *ibid.,* No.105, pl.146; see No.74) and was sent to the Continent to portray King Henry VIII's prospective brides in 1538 and 1539. The King also appeared in the mural painting at Whitehall mentioned above, and in the portrait group representing the members of the Barber Surgeons Company (*c.*1541/2; the finished version, mainly executed by studio assistants, still belongs to the Company, and another, painted over Holbein's original cartoon for the heads, is owned by the Royal College of Surgeons).

In England Holbein is today known almost exclusively for his portraits. There was probably little demand for religious paintings after the Reformation, but at the start of his second visit to this country he executed two large canvases depicting allegories of Riches and Poverty for the German Steelyard (now lost), and for the same body he apparently designed a triumphal arch for the Coronation procession of Queen Anne Boleyn. During his time in England he learnt the art of miniature painting from Lucas Horenbout (Nos.89 and 90), and made a large number of designs for goldsmith's work and for other decorative objects such as seals, Garters, hat badges and swords.

There was evidently no shortage of work for an artist of Holbein's skill, for at this time portraiture played a recognised part in diplomacy and marriage negotiations: the King had on occasion commissioned portraits from other artists, such as Lucas Horenbout (Nos.89 and 90) or perhaps Joos van Cleve (No.50). However, the same was not the case with the members of the court, for whom Holbein's second visit provided a great opportunity: it is highly probable that for many this was the first time they had sat for a portrait. Several courtiers had recently travelled to the courts of France and Italy, and some, such as Sir Thomas Elyot (No.31), were aware that England lagged behind in the patronage of the visual arts. They must have been eager to commission work from an artist of Holbein's stature.

Holbein's sitters included men in government as well as the principal members of the court. In particular he seems early to have gained the confidence of Thomas Cromwell (whose portrait is known from a version in the Frick Collection, New York; Ganz, *Paintings*, No.81, pl.125), the most powerful figure in

9

Henry's administration after the fall of Wolsey in 1529. Cromwell was a cultivated man and could foresee the role which an artist such as Holbein might play in the campaign of propaganda in favour of the Reformation, the greatest achievement of which was perhaps Holbein's majestic image of Henry VIII. It is significant that although no drawings of Cromwell survives by Holbein, there are many portraits of his adherents (*e.g.* Nos.23, 40 and 75).

Apart from these men, nearly all Holbein's sitters came from a closely knit aristocratic group; they knew each other well, married into each other's families and attended the major court functions together. Most held some official position at court, a few of which were politically important; those appointed to positions in the Privy Chamber were personally closest to the King. The sitters included members of the two greatest noble families at court, the Howards (Nos.32–37) and the Brandons (Nos.20, 64, 85 and 86). They also included some of those who were most active in introducing the new art of the Renaissance to England, usually through France with which diplomatic relations were close. The tomb of the 3rd Duke of Norfolk (No.37) at Framlingham is a fine example of the style evolved under François I; Sharington (No.65) rebuilt his newly-acquired house, Lacock Abbey, in a more advanced style in the 1540s; and Sir Philip Hoby (No.67) was buried – together with his brother Thomas, the translator of Castiglione's *Courtier* – in a tomb at Bisham, Berkshire, which bears their two effigies in the style of the French sculptor Pierre Bontemps.

Holbein does not seem to have repeated the large group portrait of the More family type, but he painted and drew several portrait pairs of husbands and wives (*e.g.* Nos.30 and 31, 56–57 and 59, 67 and 68, and 75 and 76): the drawings often reveal the existence of a pair when one of the paintings is lost. Some courtiers sat to Holbein more than once (*e.g.* Nos.56 and 57), and the Earl of Surrey perhaps more often than anyone else (Nos.32 and 36).

Different branches of the family might receive versions of the portrait, probably by a lesser hand; Holbein must have had a large studio to help him keep up with the courtly demand for portraits. The products of his studio lie at the start of the long tradition of the family portrait which hung in the homes of the English aristocracy.

The present exhibition includes seventy out of the total of eighty-five drawings catalogued by Sir Karl Parker in 1945. Some of those that have been excluded are school works, while others are too poor in condition to merit inclusion.

The history of the drawings by Holbein in the Royal Collection, like that of the Leonardos, is exceedingly complicated. At Holbein's sudden death of the plague in 1543 it is probable that these drawings remained, with the rest of the artist's effects, in his studio at Whitehall. The first certain record of the volume containing the drawings occurs in an inventory 'of the goods of John, Lord Lumly', compiled in 1590. The relevant passage reads as follows: 'A great booke of Pictures doone by Haunce Holbyn of certeyne Lordes, Ladyes, gentlemen and gentlewomen in king Henry the 8: his tyme .... wch booke was King Edwards the 6'. This reference informs us that the drawings belonged to King Edward VI, and suggests that the undated entry in the accounts of the King's Master of the Revels, Sir Thomas Carwarden, 'for a peynted booke of Mr Hanse Holby making 6 li', might indeed refer to their purchase. At King Edward's death in 1553 the book passed, either by gift or by purchase, to his Lord Chamberlain, Henry Fitzalan, Earl of Arundel, on whose death in 1580 it devolved on his son-in-law, Lord Lumley, whose property was listed in the inventory quoted above. When Lumley died in 1609, the book was acquired – together with other books from Lumley's library – by Henry Prince of Wales, the elder son of King James I. On Prince Henry's death three years later his library passed to his younger brother, later King Charles I. At some date between 1627 and 1630 the King gave the book to his Lord Chamberlain, the Earl of Pembroke, in exchange for Raphael's painting of St George and the Dragon now in Washington. Lord Pembroke immediately gave the volume to his brother-in-law, Thomas Howard, Earl of Arundel, the great collector and enthusiastic admirer of Holbein's work, in whose ownership several of the sheets were engraved by Hollar. Arundel went abroad in 1642, first to Holland and then to Italy where he died in 1646, but it is not known whether he took the drawings with him. They probably belonged to his widow who died in Holland in 1654, but nothing precise is known of their history until they are referred to as being once again in the Royal Collection in the version of Edward Norgate's discourse on *The Art of Limning* included by Alexander Browne in his *Appendix to the Art of Painting in Miniature*, published in 1675. It is therefore almost certain that they were bought by King Charles II and it has been plausibly suggested that the purchase was made on the advice of Sir Peter Lely, one of the greatest collectors of drawings of the period.

From this time onwards the Holbeins remained in royal possession but their history was not uneventful. In 1727 Queen Caroline of Ansbach, wife of King George II, who had come to the throne in that year, found them in a bureau at Kensington Palace in which they had been kept together with drawings by Leonardo and other artists. The Queen ordered them to be taken out of the book, framed, glazed and hung in her apartment at Richmond Lodge, her favourite residence (later destroyed) in the Old Deer Park at Richmond. At some date after Queen Caroline's death in 1737 the drawings were moved back to Kensington Palace where they were seen by George Vertue and Horace Walpole. Vertue in fact intended to reproduce them as engravings, and he and J. F. Müntz made tracings of a number of them on oiled paper, which survive at Sudeley Castle; the stains on some of the drawings appear to have been made during this process. At this time No.43 in the present exhibition was not part of the Royal Collection and was only incorporated in it in the nineteenth century. This is not to deny that this drawing was formerly part of 'the great booke', for it almost certainly was, together with six other drawings which are today scattered through the public and private collections of Europe. In No.43, as in the drawings of the unnamed lady in the British Museum, and of Thomas Wriothesley in the Louvre (Ganz, *Drawings*, Nos.93 and 87), the figure is cut around like a silhouette. Another group of drawings comprises Count Morette in Dresden, the Anonymous Man in Berlin, and the so-called Anne Boleyn formerly in Lord Bradford's collection and now in the British Museum (*ibid.*, Nos.38, 90, and 39): the corners of each of these three drawings are trimmed in the same characteristic manner. It is not known exactly when these drawings were separated from their companions at Windsor, but it is certain that another Holbein portrait drawing, that of Lord Abergavenny, formerly part of the same book, was removed from it during the volume's brief passage through Lord Pembroke's collection in the early seventeenth century: it is still preserved at Wilton House (*ibid.*, No.37). Other drawings dating from Holbein's periods of residence in England, such as the portrait of the unknown scholar or cleric at Chatsworth (S. A. Strong, *Reproductions of Drawings . . . at Chatsworth*, London, 1902, No.26), might also originally have formed part of the book, although there is no certain evidence to substantiate this claim.

Meanwhile, during the early years of the reign of King George III the Holbein drawings in the Royal Collection were taken out of their frames and stuck on to the pages of two volumes which were placed in the King's new library at Buckingham House. Here they were copied in stipple engraving by Francesco Bartolozzi, published by the Royal Librarian John Chamberlaine between 1792 and 1800 with biographical notes by Edmund Lodge, Lancaster Herald. During the nineteenth century the drawings were moved to Windsor with the rest of the drawings in the Royal Collection, now greatly increased by King George III's purchases. Soon afterwards they were again removed from the volumes and stuck down on thick sunken mounts. Recently they have been taken off these mounts, for both the old glue and the chemical content of the mounting board have been found to be harmful to the drawings, and they are now mounted between two panes of acrylic sheeting for their better preservation.

As might be expected the drawings have suffered in their disturbed history and, partly because the chalk drawing has been badly rubbed, from a very early date they have been frequently retouched and worked over. One eminent scholar, Paul Ganz, went so far as to maintain that all the pen-work that we now see was added after Holbein's day, a position that is manifestly untenable in the face of such vigorous handling as can be seen in the portraits of the Earl of Wiltshire (No.34) or of the unknown man (No.38), or in the scribbled sketches and colour notes on Northampton (No.53), but it is equally certain that in some draw-ings, such as Lady Hoby (No.68) and Thomas Wentworth (No.24), the outlines have been strengthened. Wherever possible the exist-ence of retouching will be indicated in the catalogue entries, though it must be emphasized that such observations are bound, to some extent, to be based on subjective judgements. Unfortunately attempts to distinguish old from new drawing by scientific methods have not yet yielded any information.

In writing his catalogue of the Holbein drawings at Windsor, to which the present catalogue is in so many ways indebted, Sir Karl Parker made the crucially important discovery that, like Leonardo, Holbein was left-handed. This means that he naturally drew his hatching from the upper left to the lower right corner of the area he was shading, whereas a right-handed artist draws it from upper right to lower left. We therefore have a valuable criterion to help us decide whether a drawing ascribed to Holbein is an original or a copy – leaving out of account the theoretical possibility that the copyist himself might have been left-handed.

The Windsor drawings were made during both of Holbein's periods of residence in England. Those of men and women connected with Erasmus, that is the members of the More family, Warham and Guildford (Nos. 1–3, 7–12 and 14), certainly date from his first visit and are executed on white paper almost entirely in chalks, with some watercolour washes but without ink. It is possible to form a corpus of drawings connected with portraits definitely produced during the second period, which are drawn on pink prepared paper. This does not however mean that we can distinguish with certainty the portraits made during the two visits by technical criteria alone. Holbein, like his father and brother, had in his earlier career used primed paper, and although it has usually been assumed that his use of the thicker pink priming did not begin until his second visit to England, drawings such as that of John Fisher (No. 15) and possibly even John Colet (No. 77) should perhaps not be excluded from the first period solely because they are drawn on pink grounds.

In many of the drawings on pink prepared paper the facial features are still modelled in coloured chalks, sometimes touched with watercolour, but they are flatter and less plastic than those on white paper. It has been suggested that this difference may be due to Holbein's use of a device for tracing the outlines of the head on a piece of glass placed between the artist and the sitter and, though there is no proof that Holbein actually followed this practice, the idea is convincing, as the method was described by Dürer in detail and was certainly current in Holbein's time. Dürer recommended its use to artists who felt unsure of their skill, but in Holbein's case the reason is more likely to be that he was in a hurry because his models were reluctant to sit for long periods. To modern minds the idea is slightly suspect as being an unfair short-cut, analogous to the use of photography.

But as Sir Karl Parker points out in his introduction to the Holbein catalogue one could apply to it what Sickert said of the use of photography, that it 'may be an occasional servant to a draughtsman, which only he may use who can do without it', and Holbein could certainly claim to come into this category. It may well be, however, that an audience of the 1970s is less likely to be affected than one of the 1950s, for whom Parker wrote, by the Romantic heresy that the employment by the artist of any 'mechanical' device was a sort of *dérogation de noblesse*, and apology is perhaps no longer necessary.

Very few records of the portrait painter's practice in this period survive, but one of these concerns Holbein. In March 1538 he was sent to Brussels with Sir Philip Hoby (No.67) to portray Christina, Duchess of Milan, as Henry VIII was contemplating marriage with her. The Duchess consented to have her portrait taken – although she refused to marry the King – and Holbein was granted a sitting of 'but three hours space', which was evidently long enough for the result was considered to be 'very perfect'. This three-hour sitting must have resulted in a drawing; the full length, life-size painting which would have been worked up afterwards is in the National Gallery, London (Ganz, *Paintings*, No.98, pl.139). The Windsor drawings provide a fairly extensive record of such sittings over several years.

Jan van Eyck, who worked in the early fifteenth century, is the first artist in Northern Europe known to have made detailed drawings before beginning a painted portrait; these were made in metalpoint on coated paper, a medium Holbein himself used throughout his career, but latterly only for details (*e.g.* in No.44). By the early sixteenth century artists such as the Germans Lucas Cranach the Elder and Albrecht Dürer were making bold drawings in chalks and watercolours for their own sake; Dürer in his 'Netherlandish Diary' records how he sketched people *en route* and gave these quickly made portrait drawings to the sitters concerned. The survival of drawings which Holbein made in Basel, along with the completed paintings, suggests that his preparatory drawings were valued in their own right. The experimentation with different media and the freedom in execution seen in the English drawings is characteristic of the interest shown in portrait drawings by Northern artists of the sixteenth century.

When, as was normally the case with Holbein, the final intention was to produce a painted portrait, the likeness had somehow to be transferred to the surface to be painted. One method of doing this was to prick the outlines of the drawing and blow charcoal dust through the holes, but as only one drawing in the Windsor series, that of Sir Thomas More (No.1), is pricked for transfer, this would not appear to have been Holbein's normal method. Nor are the drawings heavily scored, as would have been the case had Holbein transferred the outlines of the drawings on to the panel by pressure with a metal point or other instrument. The close comparison of drawings with the relevant paintings in the Royal Collection (Nos.12 and 13, 28 and 29) reveals that whilst the painting of Reskimer's head corresponds very closely in measurement with the drawing, in the case of Sir Henry Guildford the painted head has been made several centimetres larger than the drawing. Thus it seems that Holbein did not always rely on a method of direct transference of outlines to the panel. It was more important to him to copy the details of a drawing, particularly the nuances of light and shade which could only be gleaned from direct observation during a sitting; these carefully observed details, faithfully translated into paint, make Holbein's faces come alive. He was able to make alterations in size or pose at will during the course of painting, and the details of costume could of course be added afterwards.

The survival of so many drawings from this period is exceptional and is due to the fact that they were passed on in a collection, as the 'great booke'; but few of the paintings made from the drawings survive. The photographic section of this exhibition displays photographs of pictures outside the Royal Collection connected with the Windsor drawings, and gives some idea of the type of portrait painting which resulted from the drawing, although in several cases a copy or studio work is all that remains.

Whilst the Holbein series at Windsor is perhaps the best of its type, a few other comparable collections exist. The group in Berlin of sixty-nine studies of Augsburg citizens, mostly members of the burgher class, by Holbein's father constitutes one such series. Another important and analogous series of drawings, now in the Musée Condé at Chantilly, is that made by Jean Clouet (died 1540/1), an almost exact contemporary of Holbein. Clouet's sitters include members of the French royal family and house-

11 Sir Henry Guildford (No. 13)

III Derich Born (No. 25)

hold, related foreign dignitaries and Humanist scholars. Although the coverage of the two artists is much the same, the style is different. Clouet's portraits are more monumental; his sitters have a grave, almost abstract, grandeur: they belong to the classical tradition that recurs so frequently in French art. Psychologically, however, it could be argued that Holbein has the advantage, for Clouet's drawings lack the minute observation of character, feature and dress which is the hall-mark of Holbein's drawings. The sensitive drawing of the costume in the portrait of an unknown gentleman (No.38) would have disturbed the simplified form of Clouet's portraits, and he never included a pose as informal as that of John More the Younger (No.7). He would not have understood Holbein's interest in the wrinkles on Warham's face (No.14), or the tiny scars on the forehead and neck of Sir Richard Southwell (No.23) which Holbein recorded with such naturalism that until now they have been thought to be tears in the paper of the drawing. Nor would Clouet have been interested in rendering the slyness of Clinton (No.54), the obstinate arrogance of Surrey (Nos.32 and 36), the remote grandeur of Bedford (No.27) or the feline charm of Lady Parker (No.47).

Jean Clouet's son, François, who died in 1572, produced a second series of portrait drawings of the French court in a manner which was carried on until well into the seventeenth century by a succession of followers of decreasing ability. (It is interesting to note that among the items listed by Van der Doort in King Charles I's collection was a book of forty-nine portraits 'in dry cullors of the Cheifest Nobility and famous men at the tyme in ffraunce', which the King had acquired from the Duc de Liancourt.) The drawings by François Clouet are however fundamentally different in character from those of both his father and Holbein; they were intended as works complete in themselves and were made to satisfy a fashion for assembling collections of portrait drawings, which became widespread in the late sixteenth-century France. The Windsor Holbeins, like the series by François Clouet, had the names of the sitters inscribed on them, sometimes inaccurately. The English identifications were, according to the Lumley Inventory, made on the authority of notes by Sir John Cheke, tutor to King Edward VI, at a date which cannot be exactly established. While some of the names on drawings from the first English period are demonstrably wrong, the inscriptions have mostly been accepted and they served to transform the sketches into a 'collection' of the type made popular in France by the Clouets.

It is easy today to view the Holbein drawings at Windsor as a consciously planned series, but this was surely not the way in which an artist such as Holbein approached them: the individuality of each sitter presented a new challenge. Holbein's portraits, both painted and drawn, tend to concentrate on faces. Few of his sitters are shown at full-length, notable exceptions being King Henry VIII and his family in the Whitehall mural. Nor was Holbein interested, like the Flemish painter Metsys (No.5), in providing detailed and characteristic backgrounds to his portraits. He was certainly influenced by Metsys's introduction of this kind of detail into the portrait, as can be seen in his Hans of Antwerp (No.22) and in the portraits of other Hanseatic merchants as well as in the double portrait of the so-called 'Ambassadors' in the National Gallery, London, but a different approach was necessary for members of the court.

Holbein was surely more successful than any other sixteenth-century court painter north of the Alps in creating a brilliant balance between surface display and depth of characterisation, and he achieved this by focusing on the sitter alone. The drawings show the preparatory stages, recording the richness of the fabrics he was to paint – fur, satin, velvet – and, more importantly, noting down not only the lineaments of the face but also its expression, particularly the gaze of the eyes which is never the same in any two drawings.

Holbein, like his father before him, was working in the great North European tradition of portrait painting which required the artist to concentrate on the outlines of the individual face, a tradition some Italians had copied and then abandoned, scorning its literalness. Northern artists responded differently to the new challenge from the Italians: Cranach developed an extremely sophisticated emphasis on line, pattern and colour, which Holbein to some extent shared, whilst Dürer learnt a new quality of generalisation, to which Holbein also responded. But where some lesser artists were overwhelmed by Italian novelties, Holbein limited himself to an idea for a pose or the copying of an architectural motif. Although he adhered to some Northern traditions – for example he would use gold paint, to splendid effect, in quantities which would have seemed old-fashioned to the Italians (*e.g.* No.13) – he could also create an illusion of immense richness and elegance, rivalling Titian or Bronzino, using dark, restrained colours (*e.g.* in No.25).

Sometimes Holbein experimented with a particular pose, such as the original and vivid attitude of John Poyntz in No.51, or with the classical profile view, in Nos.39 and 55, but more often he was content with a three-quarters or even a simple frontal view, as is the case with many of the court ladies, a pose which could make the sitter appear massive and even overpowering, as when developed from Guildford (No.13) through to King Henry VIII (No.82) and Norfolk (No.37).

Although in the final painting, as with other court artists, the costume of the sitter received a good deal of emphasis, this was not at the expense of achieving a vivid semblance of reality in the facial features. It was common practice in the sixteenth-century for court artists to work up a portrait from another artist's inferior likeness. Holbein's drawings show that he would never have been content with this: even when working from a piece of sculpture (No.77) he shows his interest in the qualities which make a face lively and not merely a good likeness.

Holbein developed the illusion of verisimilitude to an un-paralleled degree of sophistication, and his paintings are full of devices which draw attention to the marvels of the painter's art, such as inscriptions which defy the illusion of the space occupied by the sitter, or which, as in the Derich Born portrait (No.25), challenge the onlooker to distinguish reality from the painted surface. Yet for all the final polish the sitters are often wary and watchful, as though conscious of our gaze; this immediacy Holbein caught in his drawings and, despite the damage most have suffered, they still speak to us as if they were people we knew.

Looking at the English court through Holbein's drawings from Windsor, it is not difficult to understand the enthusiasm with which Erasmus wrote to Sir Thomas More's daughter, Margaret Roper, on 7th September 1529, saying he could hardly express his delight at Holbein's drawing 'which showed me your whole family almost as faithfully as if I had been among you'.

Some notes on the Dress in Holbein's Portraits

Meticulously represented by Holbein, heavy, sumptuous and surprising to contemporary foreigners (for whom English fashions were hopelessly out of date), the dress of Holbein's English ladies has still not been studied for its own sake. The Wardrobe accounts for the period have never been published so it is impossible to date the costumes precisely, but the Windsor drawings are undoubtedly the most important visual source for English dress in the 1520s and 1530s. Holbein is himself the best, but not the only, witness to portray the contraptions of linen, steel, velvet and more mysterious ingredients held firmly to feminine upper-class English heads, for in remote and now decaying Suffolk churches, far from the royal drawing rooms, are brasses of country ladies of the middle 1520s wearing almost identical head-dresses.

Nevertheless it is Holbein, with his eye for the exact placing of a pin or for the slight swelling on an outer layer produced by a metal spring beneath (*e.g.* No.16), who will always be the key to this formidable fashion. Sometimes, as in the drawing of Lady Ratcliffe (No.62), he floats into the background sketches both of the ornamental fretwork to complete a head-dress, and of the embroidery which would have decorated the standing collar-band of a barely visible alternative chemise which he, or his sitter, might finally prefer. Sometimes alternative jewellery is suggested (*e.g.* No.53) and sometimes a background detail describes an ornament or two for a gentleman's cap – thin trifles of silver-gilt, reminiscent (perhaps nostalgically) of the *bezants* and *aiguilettes* of the fourteenth century (*e.g.* on the cap of No.12).

Apart from their caps, some of them so extremely flat, the dress of the gentlemen is nearer to the international fashion than the dress of the ladies. This had always been the case, for men travelled while women on the whole did not. Everywhere in the North of Europe women wore hoods, or veils arranged to look like them, but the strange jewelled gable (*e.g.* Nos.33 and 59) that supported the English version was indigenous. Underneath, ladies wore a linen coif or cap and at least one other layer held to the head by means of a metal spring. The hair was concealed at the front by striped bands (*e.g.* No.59) and foreigners complained that it was impossible to tell whether English ladies were dark or fair. The drawing of an Unknown Lady (No.48) gives an idea of what the assembled head-dress might have looked like before the gable was attached. Holbein explained, in a drawing now in the British Museum (Ganz, *Drawings*, No.150), what these English hoods, which often had two hanging ends, looked like from the back. It was a fashionable fancy to throw one end up over the head (*e.g.* Nos.33 and 62). The late Herbert Norris made a valiant and partially successful attempt to analyse these head-dresses, but the key to their complex structure almost certainly lies in an agglomeration of fragmentary comments hidden in early sixteenth-century plays, romances, gossipy letters, disapproving sermons, satirical poems and unpublished Wardrobe accounts which have not, up to the present, been studied from this point of view. It might be unwise to assume that the ladies drawn by Holbein wearing hoods or veils which were *not* black (*e.g.* Nos.16 and 17) belonged to a different country or to a different social class. Hoods much simpler, or of a different material, may merely have been worn on a different social occasion, at a different time of the day or by a wearer with a different taste in dress (*e.g.* No.43). At the same time both the dress and the stiff veil of the Unknown Lady (No.17) do look remarkably Netherlandish.

As for the dress itself, both men and women wore three basic garments, all three visible when worn by people of fashion. These were the shirt or chemise, the under-tunic or under-dress and the over-tunic or over-dress. Most but by no means all men wore a shirt with a high neck-band which was often embroidered (*e.g.* No.56); Thomas Boleyn (No.34) for instance does not. The chemises of the women too could be cut high to the neck (*e.g.* No.49) or low across the bosom (*e.g.* No.21) and in either case the shoulders were frequently covered by a short shoulder-piece – thick, made perhaps of velvet, or thin, certainly of linen (*e.g.* No.9).

The discovery of a few hairs of the fur that lined a slashed sleeve (*e.g.* in No.53), of a pin or two to hold a shoulder-piece in place (*e.g.* in No.9), or of the metal end of what the Dutch, who wore them into this century, called an ear-iron (*e.g.* in No.48), is often a reward for peering into these drawings, done at a moment when all over Europe people were becoming increasingly aware of each other's fashions; an awareness echoed, or perhaps initiated, by Holbein, Dürer and the Swiss painter Niklaus Manuel Deutsch. In 1560, seventeen years after Holbein's death, Bertelli published in Venice the first of what was to be a succession of illustrated books on the dress of the peoples of Europe by authors of different nationality. By the end of the sixteenth century these books also included the dress of Africans and Americans.

A Note on Watermarks

The serious study of the watermarks on Holbein's drawings at Windsor has hardly begun (they were photographed for the first time only in 1978), but a few preliminary remarks may be made. Thirty-five out of the seventy drawings exhibited here bear watermarks and, where possible, the corresponding Briquet numbers have been indicated in the catalogue. Comparisons with the unpublished records of the watermarks made in 1915–16 by F. W. Barry, a member of the Royal Library staff, show that several more have been discovered since then. An attempt was made by Ganz in his catalogue of Holbein's drawings to describe the watermarks, but the results are on the whole extremely unreliable. Any new assessment of the watermarks has been much facilitated by the new method of mounting the drawings, so that they are now easier to see than ever before.

Approximately fourteen different types of watermarks are visible and although it is not at the moment possible to draw any firm conclusions as to the date of the drawings from the watermarks, there is nothing to suggest any contradictions in the present distribution of the drawings in the periods of Holbein's first and second visits. Whereas (with one exception, No.1) the drawings of the More family which have watermarks (Nos.2, 3, 8 and 9, along with No.16) share the same watermark, this reappears on drawings such as that of the Earl of Southampton (No.26), which is definitely from Holbein's second visit. It is thus dangerous to use the watermarks rigidly as a criterion for assigning drawings to one period or another. The controversial drawing of Fisher (No.15) provides a further *caveat* for it bears a watermark found on no drawing which certainly dates from the first visit (*i.e.* the More family drawings and Nos. 12 and 14), but this is not to say that it cannot be a first period drawing.

There is an interesting observation to be made in the case of pairs of drawings where the sitters are husband and wife. When both drawings bear watermarks, these are invariably identical; this is true of the Riches (Nos.75 and 76) and of the Hobys (Nos.67 and 68) which tends to bear out the suggestion that the latter are indeed a pair.

Finally, the watermarks show that the paper which Holbein used for most of these drawings was of a variety commonly found in England in the 1520s and 1530s, and which was imported, mainly from France. Some of the watermarks found on the Holbein drawings at Windsor are also to be found on the contemporary State Papers in the Public Record Office in London.

IV Sir John Godsalve (No. 40)

v Mary Zouch (No. 45)

VI Lady Audley (No. 83)

VII Unknown Lady (No. 84)

VIII Henry Brandon,
2nd Duke of Suffolk (No. 85)

IX Charles Brandon,
3rd Duke of Suffolk (No. 86)

x Solomon and the Queen of Sheba (No. 88)

Catalogue

Every item is by Holbein unless otherwise indicated. Height precedes width. All drawings are on white paper unless stated otherwise. The Royal Library inventory number is denoted by the initials 'R.L.'. Owing to the practical problems of arranging the exhibition it has not been possible to hang the works in strict chronological order but the drawings and paintings connected with Holbein's first visit to England (1526–28) are shown together as Nos.1–16, and where possible portraits of members of a single family have been kept in one group.

Studies for the More family group portrait (1–3, 7–11)

The Royal Library contains eight drawings made by Holbein in preparation for the group portrait showing Sir Thomas More and his family which was painted on his first visit to England in 1526–28. The original picture is lost, but the composition is known from copies, the best being that at Nostell Priory, Yorkshire, and from a drawing sent by Holbein to Erasmus, who had first introduced the artist to More (see Strong, NPG, pp.345–51; NPG, *More*, Nos.1 and 169). The drawing contains notes by Nicolaus Kratzer, mathematical tutor in More's household, identifying all the sitters; it has remained in Basel since the artist sent it there in 1528 or 1529. The three sitters who appear in the group portrait but are absent from the Windsor series are Margaret Roper, Sir Thomas More's eldest daughter, his second wife Alice and the household jester Henry Patenson.

1 Sir Thomas More

Black and coloured chalks. Pricked for transfer. 397×299 mm. Inscribed: *Tho: Moor Ld Chancelour*. Briquet 1827 (R.L.12268; Parker 3).

Born in London 1477/8, Sir Thomas More was perhaps the noblest figure of King Henry VIII's reign. A great Humanist, he wrote *Utopia* in 1515–1516, in which he set forth the principles of his ideal society. From the end of the last decade of the fifteenth century More was a friend and correspondent of Erasmus (Nos.5 and 6) and it was through him that More met and became friends with Colet (No.77), Warham (No.14) and Fisher (No.15). As a lawyer and politician he had a brilliant career and became Lord Chancellor in 1529 in succession to Cardinal Wolsey. More resisted the King's project for divorcing Katherine of Aragon and in 1532 he voluntarily relinquished the

1 Sir Thomas More

Chancellorship. Two years later he refused to take the Oath on the Act of Succession which acknowledged Henry as Supreme Head of the English Church. On 17th April 1535 he was sent to the Tower where he was interrogated by Thomas Cromwell and his agent, Richard Rich (No.75). More was condemned to death on a charge of treason, largely on perjured evidence given by Rich and he was beheaded five days later, on 6th July 1535. He was beatified in 1886 and canonised in 1935.

More's family life was as important to him as his public career. In 1505 he married Jane Colt who bore him four children, Margaret

2 Sir Thomas More

Roper and those shown in Nos. 7, 10 and 11. Jane died aged 23 in
1511 and More married again, this time a widow, Alice Middleton,
who outlived him. Holbein is thought to have stayed with the More
family at Chelsea during his first visit to England.

This drawing is one of Holbein's most penetrating character studies
and though worn it is one of the least retouched sheets in the whole
series. It is closely connected with the portrait in the Frick Collection,
New York (see S. Morison and N. Barker, *The Likeness of Thomas More*,
London, 1963 and Strong, NPG, pp.227–230).

Iudge More Sr Tho: Mores Father.

3 Sir John More

2 Sir Thomas More

Black and coloured chalks, and watercolour wash. 376×255 mm.
Inscribed: *Sier Thomas More*, in a contemporary hand. Briquet 12863
(R.L.12225; Parker 2).

For biographical notes see No.1. This drawing is much feebler than
No.1, and its attribution to Holbein has sometimes been doubted, but
it is so close to the group drawing in Basel that his authorship seems
inescapable. Some of the outlines have been retouched and the wash
in the hat has been added later.

4 Johannes Froben

3 Sir John More

Black and coloured chalks. 350×273 mm. Inscribed: *Iudge More S*ʳ
Tho: Mores Father. Briquet 12863 (R.L.12224; Parker 1).

The father of Sir Thomas More (Nos.1 and 2), John More was born
c.1451, the son of William More, a baker. He married Agnes, daughter
of Thomas Graunger, a well-to-do citizen of London. John More was a
successful barrister and became Judge of the Court of Common Pleas
in 1518 and of the King's Bench in 1523. He died in 1530.

The drawing has been slightly retouched in black chalk on the
fur collar.

4 Johannes Froben

Panel. 552×324 mm ($21\frac{3}{4} \times 12\frac{3}{4}$ ins), including a later addition at the top of 64 mm ($2\frac{1}{2}$ ins). On the other three sides the original unpainted edge is visible (Millar, No.27).

Johannes Froben (1460–1527) was one of the finest printers of his time. He was closely associated in Basel with Holbein, who produced book illustrations and decorative work for him. Erasmus lived in Froben's house in Basel and from 1514 onwards his works were printed by him.

The companion portraits of Froben and Erasmus (Nos. 4 and 6) are thought to have been bought by the 1st Duke of Buckingham from Michel Le Blond, c.1625. They were given to King Charles I by the Duke, just before he set sail for the Isle of Rhé on 27th June 1627. The CR (Carolus Rex) brand is on the addition at the top of the panel. The additions had been put on to both panels before they were entered into Van der Doort's catalogue, in which the measurements of No.4 were given as $21 \times 12\frac{1}{2}$ inches.

It is possible that the two panels had been the two parts of the diptych described in the list of Holbein's works in the Basel MS. *Humanae Industriae Monumenta* by Remigius Faesch (1595–1667), though they were never joined during the period in which they have been in the Royal Collection. X-rays show that in the original background of the Froben is a curtain of which a small part appears in the Erasmus (No.6), as if the two likenesses were set against a common background. They must definitely therefore have formed part of a diptych.

At about the time they entered the Royal Collection, imaginary perspectives were painted in the backgrounds of both portraits, probably by Hendrick van Steenwyck who was patronised by the King and the Duke of Buckingham. Vertue stated that the backgrounds had been painted in 1626, Walpole that he saw the date 1629, and Steenwyck's name, on the background of Froben's portrait. In 1927 the perspective was taken off the original background of No.4, but was not disturbed on the additional area at the top which is now concealed by the frame.

This portrait of Froben is probably the best surviving version of the portrait of the sitter which was painted by Holbein at Basel c.1522–23, and is certainly better than the companion piece (No.6). X-rays have revealed quality perhaps better than had earlier been expected. Of the versions and variants, the finest is probably the small roundel in the Merton Collection (Ganz, *Paintings*, No.54, pl.96; Museum Boymans-van Beuningen, Rotterdam, *Erasmus en zijn tijd*, 1969, No.345).

5 *Quentin Metsys* Desiderius Erasmus

Quentin Metsys (1466–1530)

5 Desiderius Erasmus

Panel. 505 × 451 mm (19⅞ × 17¾ins).

The importance of this portrait has been dramatically demonstrated by a team of scholars (Lorne Campbell, Margaret Mann Phillips, Hubertus Schulte Herbrüggen and J. B. Trapp) who completed their researches at the time of the exhibition at the National Portrait Gallery, '*The King's Good Servant', Sir Thomas More* (1977–78), and in the course of comparisons made after the exhibition was closed. The version in the Galleria Nazionale d'Arte Antica in Rome, for long held to be the original, was included in the More exhibition as No.53. Comparison established beyond doubt, however, that the Erasmus portrait in the Royal Collection is in fact Metsys's original and, with the portrait of Pieter Gillis (or Petrus Aegidius) in the collection of the Earl of

Radnor (exh. NPG, *More*, No.54), composed the diptych sent by them to Sir Thomas More as an expression of friendship in September 1517. This note is a synopsis of material, gathered by the four scholars who have worked on the problem, which is published in an article in *The Burlington Magazine* for November 1978.

Erasmus was born in Rotterdam in *c*.1466. He first visited England in 1499, when he met the Royal children (including the future Henry VIII) at Eltham. In 1505 he returned and became acquainted with William Warham (No.14). Erasmus stayed in Sir Thomas More's house (see No.1) on his third visit to England from 1509 to 1511, and there wrote his famous satire, the *Moriae Encomium* (In Praise of Folly). It was on this visit that, at the invitation of John Fisher (No.15), Erasmus lectured at Cambridge.

In 1521 Erasmus settled at Basel where he acted as editor to the publishing establishment of Johannes Froben (No.4). He never again visited England although he continued to correspond with his friends there. He died in Freiburg im Breisgau in 1536.

Erasmus and More had been friends since 1499 and when, in the spring of 1515, More set off on a diplomatic mission to the Low Countries, Erasmus commended him to another old friend, the Town Clerk of Antwerp, Pieter Gillis. Gillis and Erasmus commissioned Metsys to paint their portraits for More. By the end of May, Erasmus's likeness was under way and was probably finished before the companion portrait. Verses written by More upon the diptych were printed by Froben (No.4) in Basel in 1518 in a collection of Erasmus's letters, preceded by a rubric in which details in the two portraits are described.

Lord Radnor's portrait of Gillis has been enlarged at a later date, but the original part of the panel is almost exactly the same size as No.5. The CR (Carolus Rex) brand is to be found on both panels and both are recorded by a contemporary source as being in the collection of Charles I. All the books painted in the Gillis portrait link him with Erasmus. No.5 is not only superior in quality to the version in Rome, but, unlike that version, includes the titles of the books on the shelves (all especially significant for the period in which the diptych was being painted) and shows what Erasmus is actually writing – his paraphrase of St Paul's Epistle to the Romans, the work specifically mentioned in the rubric printed with More's verses. The handwriting is a close imitation of Erasmus's hand, written with his favourite reed pen.

The article referred to above contains an account of the physical state of this picture.

6 Desiderius Erasmus

6 Desiderius Erasmus

Panel. 546×327 mm (21½×12⅞ ins), including a later addition of 64 mm (2½ ins) at the top. On the other three sides the original unpainted edge is visible (Millar, No. 39).

For the history of this picture see the entry for the companion portrait of Froben (No.4). When recorded in King Charles I's collection, the measurements of No.6 were given as 21 × 13 inches. The perspective background, which was probably painted by Henrick van Steenwyck and which covers an original curtain of which a part is carried across the background of the pendant (No.4), has not been disturbed.

An early derivation from Holbein's portrait of Erasmus of which the

7 John More the Younger

finest version, dated 1523, is at Longford Castle (Ganz, *Paintings*, No.34, pl.64), and of which numerous versions, variants and derivations are recorded.

7 John More the Younger

Black and coloured chalks. 380 × 281 mm. Note in the artist's hand: *lipfarb brun* (complexion brown) and inscribed: *Iohn More Sr Thomas Mores Son* (R.L.12226; Parker 6).

8 Anne Cresacre

The only son of Sir Thomas More, John was born *c*.1509; in 1529 he married Anne Cresacre (No.8), his father's ward. After Sir Thomas More's execution, John More was imprisoned in the Tower but he was later released. In 1544 he was pardoned, probably for his part in a plot against Archbishop Cranmer the previous year. He died in 1547.

This drawing is worn, particularly in the right eye, nevertheless it is one of the most striking examples of Holbein's brilliant handling of black chalk as a means of giving vitality to the form of a head or of

Mother Iak.

9 Margaret Giggs

drapery. Except for the cap, it is close to the figure of John More in the Basel sketch and later painted versions of the More family group.

8 Anne Cresacre

Black and coloured chalks. 379 × 269 mm. Briquet 12863 (R.L.12270; Parker 7).

Anne Cresacre, the daughter of Edward Cresacre of Barnborough, Yorkshire, became the ward of Sir Thomas More (Nos.1 and 2) in 1512 when still a baby; she was brought up and educated with the More children. In 1527 she was betrothed to More's son, John (No.7) and two years later they married. She bore him three sons and a daughter; after John More's death in 1559, Anne married George West. She died in 1577.

The drawing is worn and retouched a little but retains an arresting combination of black and yellow chalks. Holbein appears to have sketched Anne seated, but in the Basel drawing she is shown standing.

9 Margaret Giggs

Black and coloured chalks. 379 × 269 mm. Inscribed: *Mother Iak*. Briquet 12863 (R.L.12229; Parker 8).

The foster daughter of Sir Thomas More (Nos.1 and 2), Margaret Giggs was brought up with his family. She was a Greek scholar and was also interested in medicine. In 1526 Margaret married her tutor, John Clement. After the death of Henry VIII she and her husband went into exile in Louvain. They returned under Queen Mary, but on the accession of Queen Elizabeth they again left England. The Clements settled in Malines where they died, Margaret in 1570, John in 1571.

Unlike the other female members of the More family (Nos.8, 10 and 11), Margaret Giggs wears a fur hat similar to that worn by the *Lady with a Squirrel* in Holbein's painting at Houghton Hall (Ganz, *Paintings*, No.43, pl.75). However in the Basel group drawing and the painted versions, Margaret's head-dress has been changed to the type worn by the sitters in Nos.8, 10 and 11. The 'Mother Iak' referred to in the inscription was a Mistress Jack or Jackson, nurse to Prince Edward; the reason for the identification is obscure.

The face is somewhat worn, the eyes and the end of the nose are all retouched.

10 Elizabeth Dauncey

10 Elizabeth Dauncey

Black and coloured chalks. 367×259 mm. A colour note *rot* (red) in the artist's hand. Inscribed: *The Lady Barkley* (R.L.12228; Parker 4).

The second daughter of Sir Thomas More (Nos.1 and 2), Elizabeth was born in 1506 and married William, son of Sir John Dauncey. This is the study for the figure on the extreme left of the Basel group drawing. The identification of the sitter as Lady Berkley, daughter of Sir John Savage, married to Thomas, Lord Berkeley is certainly wrong but has not been explained.

The contours of the forehead, nose and mouth have been retouched.

11 Cecily Heron

11 Cecily Heron

Black and coloured chalks. 378 × 281 mm (R.L.12269; Parker 5).

The third and youngest daughter of Sir Thomas More (Nos.1 and 2), Cecily was born in 1507 and in 1525 married Giles, son of Sir John Heron, Treasurer of the Chamber to King Henry VIII. Cecily and her sister Elizabeth (No.10) married on the same day in the same church; their two husbands both sat in the Reformation Parliament of 1529. Sir Thomas More showed his impartiality when he gave a judgement against his son-in-law, Giles Heron, in a lawsuit over which he was presiding. Heron was implicated by Cromwell in More's disgrace and was executed for treason in 1540.

Stella Mary Newton has pointed out that Cecily Heron is wearing a dress which is adapted to her pregnant condition. This previously unnoticed fact is more clearly seen in the Basel group drawing and it may be the reason why Holbein borrowed the pose from Leonardo da Vinci's portrait of Cecilia Gallerani (Czartorski Museum, Cracow) for it enabled him partially to conceal her condition with her right hand. Furthermore, Holbein has drawn Cecily seated both in this drawing, and in all the group portrait versions. In common with many of the other female sitters depicted by Holbein, Cecily Heron wears a head-dress composed of a number of different layers – certainly three and probably four – of which the outer one apparently included a strap which passed under the chin. The head-dress would be held in place by a metal hoop which gripped the side of the face; this was either threaded into the hem of one of the under layers or applied as a separate item.

This drawing has been retouched in the left eye, the veil over the shoulder and the part of the head-dress projecting beyond the left cheek.

12 Sir Henry Guildford

Black and coloured chalks with some watercolour. 384 × 294 mm. Inscribed: *Harry Guldeford Knight*. Briquet 1827 (R.L.12266; Parker 10).

For the biography of the sitter see No.13, for which this drawing is a preparatory study.

13 Sir Henry Guildford (*Colour plate II*)

Panel. 826 × 664 mm (32½ × 26⅛ ins). The panel may have been reduced on the left by *c*.44 mm (1¾ ins). Inscribed on the later *cartellino: Anno. D: MCCCCCXXVII./Etatis. Suæ. xl. ix:* (Millar, No.28).

The *cartellino* is of the distinctive type painted on to portraits in his collection by John, 1st Lord Lumley (*d*.1609); although it has been repainted, the calligraphy typical of Lumley's *cartellini* can be discerned underneath the present inscription. The portrait, with the companion portrait of Mary, Lady Guildford, is recorded in his collection. They were later in the collection of the Earl of Arundel, were taken abroad with many of his possessions and passed ultimately into the possession of William, Viscount Stafford. The portrait of Sir Henry was acquired by the Crown soon after the death of Stafford's grandson in 1734 (F. H. C. Weijtens, *De Arundel-Collectie*, Rijksarchief, Utrecht, 1971, p.30).

Guildford was a favourite of King Henry VIII and he is here shown clasping the white staff of the office of Comptroller of the Royal

Harry Guldeford Knight.

12 Sir Henry Guildford

Household (to which post he had been appointed *c.*1523), and wearing the collar of the Order of the Garter (with which he had been invested in 1526); he was also at the time Chamberlain of the Exchequer. As Comptroller he authorised payments for decorative work at Greenwich to a Master Hans, who is assumed to be Holbein, in the year in which this portrait was painted. Sir Henry was the son of Sir Richard Guild-ford and was born between 1478 and 1489. He began his career at court as Squire of the Body, rising to the offices of Royal Standard Bearer (1513), and Master of the Horse (1515–22). He attended the King at the Field of the Cloth of Gold in 1520 and died in May 1532.

13 Sir Henry Guildford

The brooch shown in his cap in this portrait is engraved with a design composed of a clock and surveying instruments, components of an iconographic formula, the 'Typus Geometriae', used by Dürer in his engraving *Melencolia I* of 1514 (Panofsky, pp.156–7).

This is one of only two portraits in oils to survive in this country from Holbein's first visit to London (the other is the *Lady with a Squirrel* in the Cholmondeley collection). The companion portrait of Lady Guildford was offered at a comparatively low price to Queen Victoria in 1886; it was not acquired and is now in the City Art Museum, St Louis (Ganz, *Paintings*, No.45, pl.78). It is interesting to note that in transferring the likeness from the drawing (No.12) to panel, Holbein appreciably lengthened the countenance. A number of copies on a small scale are recorded.

14 William Warham, Archbishop of Canterbury

14 William Warham, Archbishop of Canterbury

Black and coloured chalks, with some wash. 407 × 310 mm. Inscribed: *Waramus Arch Bᵖ Cant:* Briquet 1827 (R.L.12272; Parker 12).

Probably born 1450/65, Warham became a Fellow of New College, Oxford, in 1475, was Master of the Rolls from 1494 to 1502, became Bishop of London in 1502 and two years later was appointed Archbishop of Canterbury and Lord Chancellor. He took part in several diplomatic missions – to the Duke of Burgundy (1496–99), and to the Emperor (1499 and 1501–02). As Archbishop of Canterbury and Primate of all England, Warham clashed several times with Cardinal Wolsey, the Papal Legate, over questions of ecclesiastical authority, but together they began the proceedings for the King's divorce. When Wolsey died in 1529 Warham was left to persuade the clergy to agree to the King's wishes. He died on 22nd August 1532, shortly after making a formal protest against the divorce. Warham was Chancellor of Oxford University from 1506, and a patron of Erasmus, to whom he often sent gifts of money. Erasmus described Warham as leading a frugal and scholarly life. In 1524 he sent the portrait Holbein had made of him to Warham as a present. In return Warham commissioned Holbein to paint him in a similar pose in order to send Erasmus a complementary portrait.

The drawing is one of the most damaged, but also one of the most vivid, of the series. It was used for a painted portrait, dated 1527; the version in the Louvre is now thought to be superior to that at Lambeth Palace (see Roy Strong, 'Holbein in England, III: Archbishop Warham' *The Burlington Magazine*, CIX, 1967, pp.698–701; Strong, NPG, pp.323–4).

15 John Fisher, Bishop of Rochester

On pink prepared paper. Black and coloured chalks. Reinforced in ink with brush and pen; some watercolour wash. 382×232 mm. Inscribed in a contemporary hand: *Il Epyscopº de roscster fo . . . . . ato Il Capº lanº 1535*. Close to Briquet 11341 (R.L.12205; Parker 13).

Fisher was born in 1469 and educated at Cambridge, becoming Master of Michaelhouse in 1497. He became Vice-Chancellor of Cambridge in 1501, Chancellor and Bishop of Rochester in 1504 and in the following year he was elected President of Queen's College. Fisher was a close friend of Erasmus (Nos.5 and 6) and it was through his influence that Erasmus visited Cambridge in 1511. Like More (Nos.1 and 2), Fisher remained a resolute opponent of Luther, and his support of the Pope led him to refuse to recognise Henry VIII's supremacy. In 1534 he was imprisoned for denying the validity of the Royal divorce, attainted and executed on June 22nd 1535. Whilst in the Tower, Fisher received a Cardinal's hat; he was beatified in 1886 and canonised in 1935.

The dating of the drawing presents problems because the use of pink primed paper strongly suggests that it was executed during the artist's second English period, but Fisher was already out of favour when Holbein returned to England in 1532. Furthermore the watermark found on No.15 is not of a type found among the group of drawings made on the first visit (but see Introduction, p.23). In his catalogue, Parker dated this drawing to early in Holbein's second English period on technical grounds. This verdict should be regarded with caution as it is perhaps unwise to make rigid distinctions between the techniques which Holbein employed on his first and second trips to England (see Introduction, p.23). However, there is certainly

15 John Fisher, Bishop of Rochester

a marked difference between the application of the pink priming on No.15 and that on other primed drawings. When held against a strong light, the pink preparation on the Fisher drawing can be seen to have been laid on the paper in a much less even manner than on other primed drawings in the Windsor series.

The drawing has been crudely retouched along the jaw line in black ink. A copy in black chalk is in the British Museum (reproduced by Parker, p.39) and a version of the head only, in oils on paper, is in the National Portrait Gallery (NPG, *More*, No.214).

The sixteenth-century Italian inscription, which is unique in the Windsor series, has never been satisfactorily elucidated; in particular the sixth word is undecipherable. The sentence has been variously

16 An Unknown Lady

interpreted as having reference either to the fact that Fisher was beheaded or to some unknown event which occurred on New Year's Day 1535.

16 An Unknown Lady

Black and coloured chalks, slight traces of watercolour wash. 353 × 246 mm. Briquet 12863 (R.L.12217; Parker 9).

The identity of the sitter is not known but on stylistic grounds the drawing must be dated to Holbein's first visit to England in 1526–8. Both the costume and the head-dress in No.16 are very close to those in Holbein's drawing of an Unknown Lady formerly called Margaret Roper in the British Museum (Ganz, *Drawings*, No.93).

The drawing has been retouched a little in the outlines of the face and hat but is in general well preserved.

17 An Unknown Lady

17 An Unknown Lady

Black and coloured chalks, some stumped. 402 × 290 mm. Notes in the
artist's hand: *atless* (silk), *dam* (damask) and *rot* (red) (R.L.12273;
Parker 11).

The identity of the sitter is not known. The head-dress in this drawing
is unlike that found in any of Holbein's other portrait drawings but
it closely resembles some of the head-dresses which occur in Dürer's
Netherlandish drawings dating from his trip there 1520–1, for example
the drawing of two women from the Silverpoint Sketch Book in the
Musée Condé, Chantilly (Panofsky, pl.226), or the 1521 portrait of
his wife, now in the Berlin Kupferstichkabinett (*ibid.*, pl.262). It is
probable therefore that the lady in Holbein's drawing (No.17) is also
Netherlandish; she may have been sketched while Holbein was on his
way to England in 1526.

Nicholas Borbonius Poeta.

18 Nicholas Bourbon the Elder

18 Nicholas Bourbon the Elder

Pink primed paper. Black and coloured chalks, reinforced with pen and ink. 307 × 257 mm. Inscribed: *Nicholas Borbonius Poeta* (R.L.12192; Parker 37).

Born in Eastern France in 1503, Bourbon was a famous Humanist and a friend of Erasmus and Paolo Giovio, both of whom admired his Latin poems. In 1535 he came to England to pay homage to King Henry VIII and Queen Anne Boleyn, in gratitude for protection when he was suffering persecution in France for his religious beliefs. Margaret, Queen of Navarre and sister of François I, made him tutor to her daughter, Jeanne d'Albret, mother of Henri IV of France. Bourbon's most celebrated volume of verses, entitled *Nugae* (Trifles), elicited from Joachim du Bellay the comment: 'in toto libro nil melius titulo' (nothing in the whole book is better than the title). In a letter to Thomas Solimar, Bourbon refers to Holbein as 'Mʳ Hans, the royal painter, the Apelles of our time'. He died after 1550.

19 An Unknown Lady

This drawing was the basis of a woodcut, in reverse, dated 1535 (reproduced by Parker, p.46) which was used in various editions of *Nugae*. As in Holbein's portrait of Erasmus in the Louvre (Ganz, *Paintings*, No.36, pl.66), Bourbon is here shown writing.

19 An Unknown Lady

Pink prepared paper. Black and coloured chalks, reinforced in pen and ink and some wash. 289 × 209 mm. Annotated by the artist: *rot* (red), and *liecht rot damast* (light red damask) in the dress, *rot w* (for *weiss*, white), *S* (? for *schwarz*, black) and (??) *Gold ornament* in the head-dress (R.L. 12253; Parker 61).

This drawing exemplifies the difficulties which are involved in distinguishing Holbein's hand from that of later retouchers. The colour annotations prove that Holbein himself used ink on this draw-ing and the quality of the brushwork in the dress bears this out; how-ever, the outlining of the sitter's jaw and nose is manifestly inferior.

49

The Lady Montegle.

20 Mary, Lady Monteagle

20 Mary, Lady Monteagle

Pink prepared paper. Black and coloured chalks; reinforced in pen
and ink. 296×199 mm. Annotated by the artist: *rot dammas* (red
damask) and in red chalk *rot*; on the head-dress *rot, w* (for *weiss*, white),
and ? *G* (? for gold). Inscribed: *The Lady Montegle* (R.L.12223,
Parker 60).

Mary Brandon, the daughter of Charles Brandon, 1st Duke of Suffolk
by his second wife, Anne Browne, was born *c*.1510 and between 1527
and 1529 married Thomas Stanley, 2nd Lord Monteagle; she was the
half-sister of Henry and Charles Brandon (Nos.85 and 86). During the
1530s both Lord and Lady Monteagle were constantly at court, and
Lady Monteagle received a gift of jewelry from Queen Jane (No.46). In
1538, however, Lord Monteagle wrote to Cromwell asking for support

The Lady Henegham.

21 Mary, Lady Heveningham

over the alleged misbehaviour of his wife. She died between 1541 and 1544.

In this drawing Lady Monteagle wears around her neck a jewelled 'M' presumably for Monteagle and on her dress a medallion of what appears to be a Virgin and Child.

21 Mary, Lady Heveningham

Pink prepared paper. Black and coloured chalks, the outlines reinforced with pen and ink; some brush and wash and white heightening. 302 × 209 mm. Inscribed: *The Lady Henegham* (R.L.12227; Parker 26).

The identification of the sitter is problematic. Mary, the daughter of Sir John Shelton, did not marry Sir Anthony Heveningham until 1546 or shortly before, *i.e.* after Holbein's death in 1543. However, since some of the original identifications were certainly made after 1543 it is not improbable that Mary Shelton sat to Holbein before her marriage and that the sitter was later identified in her married name. It is unlikely that the sitter was Mary Shelton's mother-in-law, Alice Heveningham, as has been suggested, as she would have been considerably older than the lady here represented.

Mary Shelton had important court connections. Her mother was a cousin of Anne Boleyn and Governess to Princess Mary, Sir John Shelton was Steward of the Household of the Princesses Mary and Elizabeth. Mary Shelton's sister, Margaret, a lady-in-waiting to Queen Anne Boleyn, was King Henry VIII's mistress for a short period in 1536. Mary Shelton herself was a friend of the Earl of Surrey (Nos.32 and 36).

The drawing is badly rubbed and retouched, particularly in the face, and the areas of black ink work on the head-dress and bodice are much later, since in Vertue's copy at Sudeley they are covered with carefully graded chalk, going from black through greys to white.

22 Hans of Antwerp

Panel. 610 × 468 mm (24 × 18$\frac{7}{16}$ ins). On the seal which lies on the ledge in front of the sitter there is apparently the letter *W*. On the paper is written: *Anno Dns 1532 auf 26 July/Aetatis* . . . The writing on the letter in the sitter's hand cannot be deciphered (Millar, No.29).

The painting was secured in Germany by Sir Henry Vane and given by him to King Charles I: '. . . upon a Crackt board the Picture of a Merchant . . . cuting with A knife the sealing Thred . . .'

This portrait evidently depicts a merchant, and the date suggests that he might belong to the Hansa Steelyard in London, whose members were painted by Holbein in 1532–33 (*cf.* No.25), but his identity has not been satisfactorily established. Woltmann (*Holbein und seine Zeit*, vol. I, Leipzig, 1874, p.368; vol. II, 1876, pp.155–56) read the inscription on the letter as: *Dem ersamen Hannsen Von anwerpen . . . upn Stallhoff zu handen* (To the esteemed Hans of Antwerp at the Steelyard). This led to the identification of the sitter with the goldsmith and Hanseatic merchant, Hans of Antwerp (also referred to as John van der Gow), who had been in England since 1515 and was paid for goldsmith's work for the Crown between 1537 and 1547; his commissions at this time included making a set of Garter insignia for Princess Mary. Holbein designed an elaborate cup for Hans to make (Ganz, *Drawings*, No.206) and the two men evidently knew each other well since Hans was a witness to Holbein's will on October 7th 1543.

If this identification is correct, this painting would provide the first evidence of the date of Holbein's return to England, for it was pre-

22 Hans of Antwerp

sumably painted in London. This portrait, and those of George Gisze (Staatliche Museen, Berlin-Dahlem), and of a member of the Wedigh family (Metropolitan Museum, New York; Ganz, *Paintings*, Nos.61 and 65. pls.98 and 103), from a group of paintings by Holbein of Steelyard merchants dated 1532.

The seventeenth-century reference quoted above shows that the panel has been in an unsatisfactory state for a long time. Extensive repaint covers areas of lost original paint, chiefly in the cap and hair, and down the beard into the costume, in the lower left background and in the still-life on the table. However, the face, the central part of the beard, the front of the shirt, the fold on and above the right elbow, and the hands are reasonably well preserved.

23 Sir Richard Southwell

23 Sir Richard Southwell

Pink prepared paper. Black and coloured chalks. Outlines in ink, incised with a metal point. 366 × 277 mm. Notes in the artist's hand: *ANNO ETTATIS SVAE*/33 and *Die augen ein wenig gelbatt* (the eyes a little yellowish). Inscribed: *Rich: Southwell Knight.* Close to Briquet 1457 (R.L.12242; Parker 38).

The sitter was born in 1504, the son of Francis Southwell of a wealthy Norfolk family. Richard Southwell was brought up with Henry Howard, Earl of Surrey (Nos.32 and 36). In 1531 he was implicated in a murder but was pardoned on the payment of a fine of £1,000. In spite of this he established himself at the court of King Henry VIII and became Sheriff of Norfolk in 1534–35 and M.P. for the county in 1539; he was knighted in 1542. Southwell was a friend of Thomas Cromwell and took an active part in the suppression of the monasteries,

L.ᵈ Wentworth.

24 Thomas, 1st Baron Wentworth

enriching himself in the process. With Richard Rich (No.75), he was one of the agents sent by Cromwell to take away the books of Sir Thomas More when he was imprisoned in the Tower, and if possible to extract some confession from him.

In 1546 he came forward as the accuser of his friend Surrey, thus initiating the proceedings which led to his condemnation and execution. Under King Edward VI, Southwell became a member of the Privy Council, but in 1549–50 he was imprisoned in the Fleet as a Catholic. He enjoyed favour under Queen Mary but on the accession of Queen Elizabeth I he lost his seat on the Privy Council. Southwell died in 1563/4.

The drawing is a study for the portrait in the Uffizi, dated 1536 (Ganz, *Paintings*, No.88, pl.131). All previous writers, including Parker, mention three small patched holes in the drawing on the neck the top of the nose and the mid-forehead, but when the drawing was

55

25 Derich Born

recently lifted from its old mount it became clear that the paper was intact at these points. In fact the 'holes' are wound scars which reappear in the Uffizi painting.

24 Thomas, 1st Baron Wentworth

Pink prepared paper. Black and coloured chalks. Reinforced with pen and ink and wash. Metalpoint in head and hat. 319 × 280 mm. Inscribed: Ld *Wentworth*. Briquet 878 (R.L.12248; Parker 79).

Born in 1501, Wentworth was a relative of Queen Jane Seymour (No.46). He took part in the campaign in France in 1523 and was knighted there. In 1527 he was head of the household of King Henry VIII's sister Mary, who was at the time Duchess of Suffolk. In 1529 he was created Baron Wentworth. A supporter of the King's divorce from Katherine of Aragon and an ardent Protestant, Wentworth converted the radical playwright John Bale. Under King Edward VI, he was a Privy Councillor and rose to the position of Lord Chamberlain in 1550. He died in 1551.

This is one of the most damaged drawings in the series, the reinforced outlines being especially clumsy.

25 Derich Born (*Colour plate III*)

Panel. 603 × 451 mm (23¾ × 17¾ ins). A little of the original unpainted edge is visible down all four sides of the panel. Inscribed on the ledge: *DERICHVS SI VOCEM ADDAS IPSISSIMVS HIC SIT/HVNC DVBITES PICTOR FECERIT AN GENITOR/DER BORN ET ATIS SVÆ 23. ANNO 1533* (Here is Derich himself: Add voice and you might doubt if the painter or his father created him). (Millar, No.26).

The CR (Carolus Rex) brand is on the back of the panel, but the portrait is not identifiable with certainty in the records of King Charles I's collection. It was, however, in Charles II's collection when it hung in the King's Closet at Whitehall. A portrait of Derich Born by Holbein was also recorded in the collection of the Earl of Arundel, among pictures from that collection which had been taken across to the Low Countries.

Derich Born, a merchant from Cologne, was a member of the Hansa Steelyard community in London (*cf.* No.22). He supplied war materials in 1536 for the suppression of the Rebellion in the North, and is recorded in London as late as 1549. A smaller portrait of the sitter, originally a roundel and painted by Holbein in the same year, is in the Alte Pinakothek in Munich (Ganz, *Paintings*, No.70, pl.117; *Alte Pinakothek: Katalog II, Altdeutsche Malerei*, Munich, 1963, p.105, No.1083).

26 William Fitzwilliam, 1st Earl of Southampton

Pink prepared paper. Black and coloured chalks. The main outlines worked over in metalpoint. 383 × 270 mm. Inscribed: *Fitz Williams Earl of Southampton*. Briquet 12863 (R.L.12206; Parker 66).

The son of Sir Thomas Fitzwilliam, William Fitzwilliam was born *c.*1490 and was brought up at court with his contemporary, King Henry VIII. He held a series of important positions in the Royal Household as well as taking part in the major military engagements against France. Fitzwilliam was knighted in 1513 and in 1522 was appointed Vice-Admiral. In 1526 he was created Treasurer of the Royal Household and elected a Knight of the Garter; in 1529 he

Fitz Williams Earl of Southampton.

26 William Fitzwilliam, 1st Earl of Southampton

became Chancellor of the Duchy of Lancaster, and in 1533 Lord Privy Seal. In 1537 William Fitzwilliam was created Earl of Southampton and in the same year resigned his post as Treasurer of the Household. He was Lord High Admiral from 1537 until 1540, and died in 1542 on his way to fight the Scots.

The original painting after this drawing was apparently destroyed by a fire in 1793. There is a copy in the Fitzwilliam Museum, Cambridge, which shows Southampton standing at full length against a landscape background, a portrait type unknown in Holbein's surviving work. In both the drawing and the painting, Southampton holds what appears to be the Staff of Office of the Lord High Admiral,

27 John Russell, 1st Earl of Bedford

which would date the drawing between 1537 and 1540: the painting,
however, bears the date 1542, the year of Southampton's death.

27 John Russell, 1st Earl of Bedford

Pink prepared paper. Black and coloured chalks, with white body-
colour in the eyes. 348 × 292 mm. Inscribed: *I Russell Ld Privy Seale with
one Eye* (R.L. 12239; Parker 69).

John Russell was born in Dorset *c*.1486, and as a young man he became
a Gentleman Usher to King Henry VII. He was favoured by the young
King Henry VIII and knighted in 1513. The King very frequently
sent him abroad on diplomatic missions, to France, and later to Italy.
In 1526 Russell was appointed a Gentleman of the Privy Chamber, and

28 William Reskimer

in 1529 he sat in the Reformation Parliament. In 1537 he was made
Comptroller of the Royal Household and two years later was created
Baron Russell and was elected a Knight of the Garter. From 1540–42
he held the post of Lord High Admiral, and then became Lord Privy
Seal. Appointed as one of the executors of King Henry VIII's will, he
continued as Lord Privy Seal under King Edward VI and Queen
Mary. In 1550 he was created Earl of Bedford. He died on March 14th
1555, and was succeeded by his son Francis (No.73).

Russell is said to have lost his right eye at the Battle of Morlaix in
France in 1522, hence the inscription on the drawing. This does not
however tally with the drawing itself, which shows both eyes, but this
appears to be due to a later alteration because in Vertue's copy of the
drawing at Sudeley Castle the sitter's right eye is clearly shown as
unseeing. There is a painted version at Woburn Abbey (Strong, NPG,
p.21).

Reskemeer a Cornish Gent:

29 William Reskimer

In this drawing Russell is shown wearing an under-cap or coif of the same type as that seen in the portraits of Thomas More (Nos.1 and 2) and the Duke of Norfolk (No.37), but without an over-cap. This under-cap is the descendent of the white late thirteenth-century coif, a high fashion which later became restricted to the wear of judges, sergeants-at-law, academics and of others holding high official posts.

28 William Reskimer

Panel. 464 × 337 mm (18¼ × 13¼ ins). The original unpainted edges have been preserved on all four sides (Millar, No.31).

The portrait of 'a side faced Gentleman out of Cornwall' was presented to King Charles I by Sir Robert Killigrew (d.1633). The CR (Carolus Rex) brand is now concealed by a later cradle. No.29 is a preparatory study for this painting.

30 Margaret, Lady Elyot

Probably painted early in Holbein's second English period *c.*1532–33. The sitter is presumably one of the sons of John Reskimer of Merthen, a member of an ancient Cornish family. The elder son, John, seems to have been engaged chiefly in local activities in Cornwall; but his younger brother William was a Page of the Chamber in 1525, and was in Wolsey's suite in 1527. He continued as a Page of the Chamber during the 1530s and in 1542 received a grant of chambers within Blackfriars. In 1546 he was made a Gentleman Usher. Reskimer died before 1564.

29 William Reskimer

Pink prepared paper. Black and coloured chalks, some metalpoint in the costume. 290 × 210 mm. Inscribed: *Reskemeer a Cornish Gent*: (R.L.12237; Parker 31).

For biographical details see No.28, for which this drawing is a study; the head is exactly the same size as in the painting.

31 Sir Thomas Elyot

30 Margaret, Lady Elyot

Pink prepared paper. Black and coloured chalks, partly stumped. Strengthened with ink, and some body-colour heightening. 278 × 208 mm. Inscribed: *The Lady Eliot*. Briquet 1050 (R.L.12204; Parker 14).

Margaret, the daughter of Sir Maurice à Barrow, married Sir Thomas Elyot (No.31) in 1522. She was said by Stapleton in his *Vita Thomae Mori* (1588) to have been a friend of learning, like her husband. Lady Elyot died on 26th August 1560.

31 Sir Thomas Elyot

Pink prepared paper. Black and coloured chalks, the outlines strengthened with ink, white heightening in the eyes. 284 × 205 mm. Inscribed: *Th: Eliott Knight* (R.L.12203; Parker 15).

Elyot was born before 1490 of a Wiltshire family of landowners, and was trained as a lawyer first at Oxford where he became a Bachelor of

Civil Law, and then at the Middle Temple. He later became Clerk to the Justices of Assize, and Clerk to the King's Council. At Oxford he also studied medicine and Greek and it may have been his love of this language which brought him into close contact with Sir Thomas More (Nos.1 and 2). In 1522 he married Margaret à Barrow (No.30).

Elyot was knighted in 1530 and in 1531 published his most famous literary work, *The Boke named the Governour*. In a letter written to Cromwell after More's execution, probably in 1536, he mentioned his former 'amity' with Sir Thomas More, but asked the addressee to forget the connection and affirmed his loyalty to the King and, by implication, to Cromwell. Elyot was Ambassador to the court of Charles V, the Holy Roman Emperor, in 1531–32. He died in 1546.

This drawing and the companion portrait of Lady Elyot are among the most vivid and best preserved of the series; they appear to have escaped any retouching. They probably date from early in Holbein's second period in England, that is to say soon after 1532.

32 Henry Howard, Earl of Surrey

Pink prepared paper. Black and coloured chalks, the outlines strengthened with pen and ink. 248 × 209 mm. Inscribed: *Thomas Earl of Surry* (R.L.12215; Parker 17).

Although the drawing is inscribed 'Thomas Earl of Surry', there is no reason to believe that this is other than Henry Howard, Earl of Surrey, the son and heir of Thomas, Duke of Norfolk (No.37). Born *c.*1517, he was educated extensively at home. From 1530 to 1532 he was the companion at Windsor of Henry, Duke of Richmond, the natural son of King Henry VIII and Elizabeth Blount, who later married Surrey's sister (No.35). Surrey himself might have married the King's daughter, Princess Mary, but instead married Frances de Vere (No.33) in 1532, though they did not live together until 1535.

From October 1532 to September 1533 (except for his presence at Anne Boleyn's Coronation in June 1533) Surrey resided at the French court with the Duke of Richmond. In 1537 he was confined to Windsor for a minor misdemeanour, but was generally in favour at court, despite the downfall in 1542 of the second of his cousins to become Queen, Catherine Howard. Surrey was elected a Knight of the Garter in 1541.

In 1542 and again in 1543 Surrey spent short periods in prison for quarrels and disturbances. From 1543–6 he took part in the campaigns in France. In December 1546 information given by Sir Richard Southwell (No.23) led to Surrey's arrest, as well as that of his father, on such charges as displaying Royal arms on his own shield, affecting foreign dress and employing an Italian jester. Surrey's sister (No.35)

32 Henry Howard, Earl of Surrey

spoke against her brother and he was eventually executed on 21st January 1547.

As a poet, Surrey is chiefly famed for introducing blank verse into the English language in his translations of parts of Virgil's *Aeneid*, and also for his adaptations of Petrarch's sonnets. Some of his most moving verses were written after the death of his friend the Duke of Richmond, lamenting the happy days they had spent together at Windsor.

None of the extant painted portraits of Surrey are related either to this drawing or to No.36. Holbein's painting of Surrey in São Paulo, Brazil shows a slightly older man, looking to the right (Ganz, *Paintings*, No.122, pl.161). The youthfulness of Surrey in this beautiful drawing would indicate a date early in Holbein's second visit, around the time of the sitter's marriage to Frances de Vere (No.33).

The Lady Surry.

33 Frances, Countess of Surrey

33 Frances, Countess of Surrey

Pink prepared paper. Black and coloured chalks, the outlines strengthened with pen and ink, and some body-colour heightening. 310 × 230
mm. Notes in the artist's hand: *rosa felbet* (rose velvet), and *felbet*.
Inscribed: *The Lady Surry*. Close to Briquet 1457 (R.L.12214;
Parker 18).

Frances de Vere, the daughter of John, 15th Earl of Oxford, was born
in 1517. In 1532 she married Henry Howard, Earl of Surrey (Nos.32
and 36). She was widowed in 1547 and at some date before 1553 married
Thomas Steynings. She died in 1577.

34 Sir Thomas Boleyn, 1st Earl of Wiltshire and Ormonde (?)

34 Thomas Boleyn, 1st Earl of Wiltshire and Ormonde (?)

Pink prepared paper. Black and coloured chalks, watercolour, ink applied with pen and brush. 401 × 292 mm. Inscribed: *Ormond.* Briquet 12863 (R.L. 12263; Parker 23).

The sitter is traditionally identified as Sir Thomas Boleyn, father of Queen Anne Boleyn and brother-in-law of the Duke of Norfolk (No.37). Born in 1477, he became Keeper of the Exchange at Calais in 1509, joint Constable of Norwich Castle in 1512, Treasurer of the Royal Household in 1522 and Lord Privy Seal in 1530. In 1525, Boleyn was created Viscount Rochford, and Earl of Wiltshire and Ormonde

67

35 Mary, Duchess of Richmond and Somerset

four years later. He died in 1539. He was a patron of Erasmus, from whom he commissioned various works.

If the sitter is Thomas Boleyn and this drawing dates from the early 1530s as has generally been assumed, then he would have to have been at least fifty-five years old, but since the sitter looks considerably younger the identification has been questioned.

The large unbroken areas of red and black watercolour make this drawing one of the most striking in the Windsor series, although the red of the hat may be a later addition. In contrast to the previous items in this exhibition, Holbein has forcefully built up the contours of the sitter's body with the point of the brush rather than black chalk, thereby achieving a sense of physical mass analogous to that seen in his portraits of King Henry VIII.

The sitter wears a full-sleeved tunic over either a short doublet or a

Ho: Earle of Surry.

36 Henry Howard, Earl of Surrey

stomacher, with slashed openings. For a somewhat similar dress see
that worn by Jean de Dinteville in the so-called *Ambassadors* portrait in
the National Gallery, London, and by King Henry VIII in the Whitehall mural (see No.81).

35 Mary, Duchess of Richmond and Somerset

Pink prepared paper. Black and coloured chalks, some black wash.
266 × 199 mm. Notes in the artist's hand: *samet rot* (velvet red) and
schwarz felbet (black velvet), and the initials *MH* and R referring to the
sitter. Inscribed: *The Lady of Richmond*. Close to Briquet 11369
(R.L.12212; Parker 16).

Mary Howard, daughter of Thomas Howard, 3rd Duke of Norfolk
(No.37) and sister of Henry Howard, Earl of Surrey (Nos.32 and 36)

69

was born in 1519. Before 1534 she married Henry Fitzroy, Duke of Richmond, natural son of King Henry VIII and Elizabeth Blount. The Duchess was an ardent Protestant. In 1547 she gave evidence against her brother at his trial. She died in 1557.

This drawing, though worn, does not seem to have been retouched, and is an exceptionally fine example of Holbein's use of the brush with black wash. It is also an interesting illustration of his working method because the line drawings and notes at the bottom of the sheet apparently suggest a variant form for the hat and indicate the initials to be embroidered on it. The fact that the colour notes state that part at least of the velvet was to be red shows that the drawing must have been made before the sitter was widowed in 1536.

36 Henry Howard, Earl of Surrey

Pink prepared paper. Black and coloured chalks, the outlines strengthened with pen and ink. 287 × 210 mm. Inscribed: *Tho: Earle of Surry*. Close to Briquet 12863 (R.L.12216; Parker 29).

The sitter is the same as that shown in No.32, for which see biographical details; he is perhaps a little older in No.36.

37 Thomas Howard, 3rd Duke of Norfolk

Panel. 803 × 616 mm (31⅝ × 24¼ ins). The inscription on the original (overpainted) green background is now almost obliterated. According to the text on the other versions it probably read as follows: *THOMAS. DVKE. OFF. NORFOLK. MARSHALL./AND. TRESVRER OF INGLONDE./THE. LXVI. YERE OF HIS AGE.* (Millar, No.30).

This portrait was acquired by Frederick, Prince of Wales, and seen in his collection by George Vertue in 1750; it was probably the version which Vertue had seen at a sale in London in 1744 which may, in turn, have been the version included in a sale in Amsterdam on 23rd April 1732. The original of the type, painted in 1538–39, was probably the painting in the possession of the sitter's great-grandson, Thomas Howard, Earl of Arundel, which was among the pictures in the inventory of the Arundel collection drawn up in Amsterdam in 1655; but that painting cannot be definitely identified with the one acquired by the Prince of Wales. A number of versions are known: at Naworth Castle, Arundel (two) and Castle Howard; full-length extensions are at Gorhambury and Arundel. Although the surface of No.37 has suffered considerably, it retains an authority and, in places, a quality which makes it superior to all of these, with the possible exception of the better of the two at Arundel. A section of the original background can be seen below the sitter's left arm.

37 Thomas Howard, 3rd Duke of Norfolk

The 3rd Duke of Norfolk (1473–1554) was closely related to the Royal house, uncle to Anne Boleyn and Catherine Howard and god-father to King Edward VI (No.74). In this painting he holds the gold baton of Earl Marshal and the white staff of Treasurer, offices he occupied from 1533 and 1522 respectively. He was also Lord High Admiral from 1513 to 1525. Norfolk was imprisoned in the Tower for High Treason in 1546 along with his son the Earl of Surrey (Nos.32 and 36), but unlike Surrey he was saved from the block by the death of the King in 1547. He remained in prison during the reign of King Edward VI, but was fully restored by Queen Mary I.

38 An Unknown Gentleman

38 An Unknown Gentleman (*Colour plate I*)

Pink prepared paper. Black and coloured chalks, and ink applied with pen and brush. 272 × 210 mm. Notes by the artist: *atlass* (silk), *at(lass)* twice and *S* (?satin). Briquet 12863 (R.L.12258; Parker 32).

One of the best preserved and most impressive drawings of the whole series, this study well exemplifies Holbein's mastery of working with a brush and ink. It is recorded in reverse in an etching by Hollar (Parthey 1547). The three names suggested for the sitter – Charles Brandon, Duke of Suffolk, Edward Stafford, Duke of Buckingham and Jean de Dinteville (the man on the left of Holbein's *Ambassadors* in the National Gallery) – are all unconvincing, but no more plausible identifications have been proposed.

39 Simon George

39 Simon George

Pink prepared paper. Black and coloured chalks, ink applied with pen and brush. 279×191 mm. Inscribed: *S George of Cornwall*. Briquet 1255 (R.L.12208; Parker 35).

Simon George's father and grandfather came from Dorset and he himself settled at Quotoule in Cornwall (misread as Quocoute by Lodge, and copied from him by Parker). Nothing is known of his connections with the court, but it would seem likely from his fashionable dress that he mixed in London society.

The drawing is connected with Holbein's painted roundel in the Städelsches Institut, Frankfort (Ganz, *Paintings*, No.104, pl.145) which shows the sitter with a full beard; but X-rays have revealed that beneath the top layer of paint the beard and hair correspond with the drawing (see O. Götz, 'Holbeins Bildnis des Simon George of Quocoute', *Städeljahrbuch*, VIII, 1932, pp.116–148).

40 Sir John Godsalve

40 Sir John Godsalve (*Colour Plate IV*)

Pink prepared paper. Coloured chalks, watercolour, body-colour, and ink applied with pen and brush. 361 × 291 mm. Inscribed (twice): *Sʳ Iohn Godsalue* (R.L. 12265; Parker 22).

Born in Norwich in *c*.1510, John Godsalve's advancement began through the friendship of his father, Thomas, with Thomas Cromwell. He became Clerk of the King's Signet *c*.1530, in which position he was Cromwell's deputy; in 1532 Godsalve was appointed to the Office of Common Meter of Precious Tissue and in this capacity he came into contact with the Hanseatic merchants who dealt in cloth and for whom Holbein was at this time working. In 1544 he took part in the Siege of Boulogne. Godsalve was knighted in 1547 and in the same year was appointed Comptroller of the Royal Mint. He died in 1556.

There is a portrait in Dresden by Holbein of Godsalve and his

41 Sir Charles Wingfield

father, dated 1528 (Ganz, *Paintings*, No.44, pl.86), but this drawing is
not a study for it. No.40 is one of the most elaborately finished of all
the drawings, containing large areas of watercolour and body-colour.
The head is well preserved but the black coat has probably been retouched by a later hand. The extensive application of a blue pigment
over the background leaves little of the pink priming exposed. The
only other drawing by Holbein which has been treated in a comparable
way is that in Basel traditionally identified as representing Prince
Edward (Ganz, *Drawings*, No.48).

Godsalve wears an outer coat of the same type as that worn by
Norfolk (No.37), in which the sleeve has a horizontal slit above the
elbow through which the arm could be passed so that the lower part of
the over-sleeve hangs down behind. The sleeve is worn at full length
by King Henry VII in the Whitehall mural (see No.81).

42 An Unknown Gentleman

41 Sir (?) Charles Wingfield

Pink prepared paper. Black and coloured chalks, some partly stumped, some strengthening in pen and ink. 282 × 197 mm. Inscribed: *Charles Winhfield Knight*. Close to Briquet 12863 (R.L.12249; Parker 36).

The drawing probably represents the son of Sir Richard Wingfield, born *c*.1514. There is no record of the sitter having been knighted and, apart from the inscription on this drawing, he is only once documented as Sir Charles Wingfield. He was a supporter of the new religious policies and in 1540 was a member of the court party sent to meet Anne of Cleves on her arrival in England. He was Sheriff of the counties of Cambridgeshire and Huntingdonshire and died in either 1540 or 1544.

The drawing is unusual in showing the sitter with his shoulders and chest naked, wearing only a medallion suspended around his neck (see No.66). It was rejected by Ganz as not being by Holbein, but though retouched appears to be basically from his hand. There is a good early copy in the Boymans-van Beuningen Museum, Rotterdam.

43 An Unknown Lady

42 An Unknown Gentleman

Pink prepared paper. Black and coloured chalks, partly stumped, some outlines strengthened with pen and black ink. 296 × 222 mm. (R.L.12259; Parker 33).

This drawing is a preparatory study for a painted roundel in the Metropolitan Museum, New York, which is dated 1535 (Ganz, *Paintings*, No.86, pl.128). The drawing has been cut on both sides and at the bottom: the hands, which are visible in the painting, have been cut off in the drawing.

43 An Unknown Lady

Two pieces of pink prepared paper (one for the figure and one for the background). Black and coloured chalks, some ink reinforcement applied with pen and brush. White body-colour heightening. 266 × 164 mm. Annotated by the artist: *Samet* (velvet), and *Damast* (damask).

44 Elizabeth, Lady Audley

Close to Briquet 12863 (R.L.12190; Parker 47).

This drawing has only been in the Royal Collection since the nineteenth century, when it was presented by Mr Humphrey Way. The known provenance goes back to the mid-eighteenth century when it was in the collection of the elder Jonathan Richardson, along with Holbein's drawing of Morette now in Dresden and the so-called 'Anne Boleyn' in the British Museum (Ganz, *Drawings,* Nos.38 and 39). Before that time all three drawings, in which the figures have each been cut around in a similar manner, may well have formed part of the 'great booke' (see Introduction, p.12).

It has been suggested that the sitter is Amelia, the sister of Anne of Cleves, who is recorded to have been portrayed by Holbein in 1539.

However, there is no evidence for this identification beyond a superficial resemblance to Holbein's portrait of Anne of Cleves in the Louvre (Ganz, *Paintings*, No.107, pl.148).

44 Elizabeth, Lady Audley

Pink prepared paper. Black and coloured chalks. Metalpoint in jewelry and writing at the bottom. Outlines reinforced in pen and ink. 292 × 207 mm. Annotated by the artist: *samet* (velvet), *rot damast* (red damask), *rot* (red), *w* (for *weiss*, white), *?Gl* (for gold), and the sign for green (small heart-shaped leaf). Inscribed: *The Lady Audley*. (R.L.12191; Parker 58).

The question of the sitter's identity has never been fully resolved. There were two families called Audley at the court of King Henry VIII. The sitter has been assumed to be Elizabeth, the daughter of Sir Brian Tuke, the Treasurer of the Chamber (portrayed by Holbein in a picture in the National Gallery, Washington; Ganz, *Paintings,* No.52, pl.88), and the wife of George Touchet, 9th Lord Audley. However, her husband did not succeed to the title until 1557.

A more likely candidate would therefore seem to be Elizabeth, the daughter of the 2nd Marquis of Dorset and his wife Margaret (the latter portrayed by Holbein in a very damaged drawing at Windsor not included in the present exhibition; Parker 28). In April 1538 Elizabeth married as his second wife Thomas, Lord Audley of Walden, who had become Lord Chancellor in 1532, and at the same time was knighted. He died in 1544; his wife married secondly in 1549 Sir George Norton. Lady Audley died before 20th November 1564.

There is no known full-size painting connected with this drawing but a miniature by Holbein survives in the Royal Collection (No.83).

45 Mary Zouch *(Colour plate V)*

Pink prepared paper. Black and coloured chalks, some stumping, some outlines strengthened with brush and ink. 294 × 201 mm. Annotated by the artist: *black felbet* (black velvet). Inscribed: *M. Souch.* Briquet 878 (R.L.12252; Parker 72).

The sitter was the daughter of John, Lord Haringworth, by his first wife. In 1527 she wrote to her cousin, Lord Arundel, begging to be taken into Royal service as her new step-mother was cruel to her. She is presumably identical with the 'Mrs Souche' who received a gift of jewelled borders from Queen Jane Seymour (No.46) and attended her funeral in 1537. As far as is known, Mary Zouch did not marry and in 1542 she was granted an annuity of ten pounds 'in consideration of her service to the King and the late Queen Jane'.

45 Mary Zouch

The letter 'M' of the inscription is possibly an abbreviation for 'Mistress' rather than a Christian name. It is unlikely, however, that the sitter is Joan, the wife of Lord Zouch's son Richard, as has been suggested, since she died around 1532. It should perhaps be noted that the second wife of Richard Zouch was named Margaret.

This is one of Holbein's most exquisitely coloured drawings and is particularly remarkable for the range of colours used, including the vivid and unusual salmon pink in the head-dress. It is very similar in the costume and the handling of the chalks to that of Grace, Lady Parker (No.47). The subject of the medallion worn by Mary Zouch cannot be positively identified but it was suggested by Chamberlain that it may represent Perseus and Andromeda (A. B. Chamberlain, *Hans Holbein the Younger*, London, 1913, vol.II, p.259).

46 Queen Jane Seymour

46 Queen Jane Seymour

Pink prepared paper, with a join 65 mm from the bottom of the sheet. Black and coloured chalks, the outlines reinforced with pen and ink. Metalpoint on clothes and headdress. 500 × 284 mm. Inscribed: *Iane Seymour Queen.* (R.L. 12267; Parker 39).

Born *c*.1509, the daughter of Sir John Seymour, Jane Seymour was a distant relative of King Henry VIII. At court she became a lady-in-waiting to Queen Katherine of Aragon, and subsequently to Queen Anne Boleyn. Whilst Anne Boleyn was still Queen, Henry VIII began to pay his attentions to Jane Seymour, and after Queen Anne's execution in 1536 the King married Jane, on 30th May of the same year. The Imperial Ambassador described her as 'of middle stature and no great beauty, so fair that one would rather call her pale than otherwise'.

47 Grace, Lady Parker

She was never crowned for she died on 24th October 1537, twelve days after giving birth to the future King Edward VI (No.74).

The only other portrait of Jane Seymour undoubtedly from Holbein's hand is in the Kunsthistorisches Museum, Vienna (Ganz, *Paintings*, No.97, pl.138). This three-quarters length painting, whilst clearly based on the drawing here exhibited, shows minor divergences from it, particularly in the jewelry and the sleeves. A portrait probably from Holbein's studio, in the Mauritshuis, the Hague (*ibid.*, No.95, pl.136), is closer to the drawing in these details. The full-length portrait of Jane Seymour in Holbein's great mural for Whitehall Palace (see No.81) must also derive from this drawing.

This rather worn study would seem, therefore, to have been used for portraits more than once, and it is possible that the two horizontal lines drawn across the sheet indicate the cut-off points for pictures of different lengths.

47 Grace, Lady Parker

Pink prepared paper. Black and coloured chalks. 298 × 208 mm. Inscribed: *The Lady Parker.* (R.L.12230; Parker 73).

Grace, the daughter of Sir John Newport, married Sir Henry Parker, the son of Lord Morley, in 1523, when aged eight. She gave birth to two sons *c.*1532 and in 1537, but she attended both Prince Edward's christening and Jane Seymour's funeral in the latter year. Her husband was Sheriff of Hertfordshire in 1536; he died in 1553, predeceasing his father, who was a friend of the Boleyns and of Princess Mary. Lady Parker died before 1549, since we know that by that date her husband had remarried.

The drawing, which is executed entirely in chalks, is in a reasonable condition and closely resembles that of Mary Zouch (No.45) in technique and costume.

48 An Unknown Lady

Pink prepared paper. Black and coloured chalks. 281 × 192 mm. Inscribed: *Anna Bollein Queen.* Briquet 11391 (R.L.12189; Parker 63).

It is most unlikely that the inscription identifies the sitter correctly. Probably the most authentic portrait of Anne Boleyn is that in the National Portrait Gallery (Strong, NPG, No.668) which is unconnected with this drawing. The drawing by Holbein now in the British Museum is no longer thought to represent her, and the inscription on that drawing is certainly not contemporary (Ganz, *Drawings*, No.39).

On the reverse of the drawing here exhibited are various heraldic sketches by Holbein, among them a coat of arms identified as that of the Wyatt family. On this basis two identifications for the sitter have been suggested. One is the sister of Sir Thomas Wyatt (Nos.80 and 81), Margaret, Lady Lee; she, however, is probably represented in the portrait attributed to Holbein in the Metropolitan Museum, New York (Ganz, *Paintings*, No.112, pl.151), in which neither the facial features nor the pose accord with those of the sitter in this drawing.

The other possibility is Sir Thomas Wyatt's wife, Elizabeth, the sister of Lord Cobham (No.66). She married Wyatt in 1520, but he

Anna Bollein Queen.

48 An Unknown Lady

repudiated her later on the grounds of her adultery. In 1542 the Imperial Ambassador described her as 'a beautiful girl' and there were hints that she might marry the King.

The sitter appears to be shown wearing an under-cap of a type that may have been worn beneath a fur bonnet such as that shown in No.9, or even a hat like that seen in No.16. The outer layer which grips the cheek almost certainly encloses a metal hoop; the additional 'prong', visible over the ear, must belong to something else which is not visible.

49 An Unknown Lady

49 An Unknown Lady

Pink prepared paper. Black and coloured chalks, bluish body-colour in the eyes. The outlines reinforced with pen and ink. 278 × 193 mm. (R.L.12254; Parker 49).

This drawing is somewhat rubbed and has been retouched.

50 *Joos van Cleve* King Henry VIII

Attributed to Joos van Cleve (d.1540)

50 King Henry VIII

Panel. 727 × 591 mm (28⅝ × 23¼ ins).

This picture was acquired in 1624 by Charles I, then Prince of Wales, from the Earl of Arundel in an exchange. It was at that time 'said to be done by Jennett', *i.e.* Jean Clouet; the attribution to van Cleve seems first to have been put forward by George Vertue at the time of King George II.

On the scroll held by the King is inscribed: *MARCI. 16/ITE IN MVNDVM VNIVERSVM ET PREDICATE/EVANGILIVM OMNI CREATVRE.* (Go ye into all the world and preach the Gospel to every creature. Mark 16, v.15). This text appears in English on the title page of Coverdale's Bible of 1535; the portrait is generally dated to the following year. It has been pointed out that the text is

51 John Poyntz

one held by the Catholic Church to support its apostolic authority
and that the portrait may have been painted even earlier in the 1530s
when the King was 'still Defender of the Faith in the sense in which he
had been granted the title'.

Joos van Cleve, a full master in the Antwerp guild of painters in
1511, was summoned to the French court in 1530. If the portrait of
Henry VIII is correctly attributed to him, one would have to assume a
visit to the English court slightly later (see Strong, *Henry VIII*,
pp.8–9; Strong, NPG, p.158, as 'Type III' in the King's iconography
and citing copies; and NPG, *More*, No.202, with bibliography).

51 **John Poyntz**

Pink prepared paper. Black chalk, partly stumped, and coloured
chalks. The outlines reinforced with pen and black ink. 295 × 233 mm.
Inscribed: *Iohn Poines*. Close to Briquet 11369 (R.L.12233; Parker 54).

52 An Unknown Gentleman

There were two men with the name John Poyntz at the court of King Henry VIII. This drawing has traditionally been identified as a portrait of John Poyntz of North Ockendon in Essex, who died on 13th June 1547.

The second John Poyntz, of Alderley in Gloucestershire, died on 29th November 1544, after accompanying the King to fight in France earlier in the year. He was the son of Sir Robert Poyntz of Iron Acton, and uncle to Sir Nicholas Poyntz (No.55). His first wife, Elizabeth, was a sister of Sir Henry Guildford (Nos.12 and 13).

The only extant painting after this drawing, in the collection of the Earl of Harrowby at Sandon Hall, comes from the family of John Poyntz of Alderley, not John Poyntz of Ockendon. Furthermore, the

53 William Parr, 1st Marquis of Northampton

identification of the coat of arms on the painting of Poyntz at Sandon Hall as that of John Poyntz of Alderley would seem to provide conclusive proof that the old identification was incorrect.

The drawing has been retouched.

52 An Unknown Gentleman

Pink prepared paper. Black and coloured chalks. Some reinforcing with pen and black ink; white body-colour in the eyes. 271 × 190 mm. (R.L.12260; Parker 44).

It has been suggested that this drawing forms a pendant to No.63 in the present exhibition.

53 William Parr, 1st Marquis of Northampton

Pink prepared paper. Black chalk, partly stumped, and coloured chalks. Extensively strengthened with ink applied with pen and brush. White heightening in the eyes. 316×211 mm. Annotated by the artist: *wis felbet* (white velvet), *burpor felbet* (purple velvet), *wis satin* (white satin). Amongst details of ornament on the left, various letters indicating colours, also *gros* (?size), and *mors* (death). Inscribed: *William Pa ... Marquis o(f) Northampton.* (R.L.12231; Parker 57).

Born in 1513, the son of Sir Thomas Parr, and brother of Catherine Parr, Queen from 1543 and 1547, William Parr was educated at Cambridge. In 1537 he was knighted and two years later was made a Baron. In 1543 he became a Privy Councillor, a Knight of the Garter and Earl of Essex. In 1547 he was created Marquis of Northampton, and three years later became Lord Great Chamberlain. But on Queen Mary's accession in 1553 he was imprisoned and deprived of his titles. Queen Elizabeth I restored them, and he prospered during her reign. Northampton married as his second wife in 1547 Elizabeth, the daughter of Lord Cobham (No.66). He died in 1571.

The Marquis of Northampton is portrayed in a costume which may have links with that of the Gentleman Pensioners (see J. L. Nevinson, *Walpole Society*, XXXIV, 1952–54, pp.1–13), of which body he was made Captain in November 1541 or 1542. The Gentleman Pensioners were a band of the King's retainers who traditionally guarded his person on the field of battle. They were required to furnish themselves with arms and usually wore a gold medallion around the neck and a hatbadge, which can be seen in Holbein's drawing.

This study is one of the most detailed of Holbein's drawn portraits with some fine ink work, but the chalk drawing has been badly rubbed.

54 Edward, 9th Baron Clinton

Pink prepared paper. Black and coloured chalks. Reinforced with (?) pencil in the line of the mouth. Metalpoint on part of the costume. 218×144 mm. Annotated by the artist: *Silb* (for *silber*, silver) or *Silk*, *Dofat* (taffeta), *S* (? for *sammet*, velvet). Inscribed: *Clinton.* (R.L.12198; Parker 42).

Edward Clinton was born in 1512 and succeeded his father as 9th Baron Clinton at the age of five. He was a ward of the King, and *c.*1530 married Elizabeth Blount, who was some years older than himself and was the mother of King Henry VIII's natural son, Henry Fitzroy, Duke of Richmond. Lord Clinton accompanied the King to France in 1532, and during the remainder of the reign participated

54 Edward, 9th Baron Clinton

both in government and in court events, such as the tournament of 1540. Under King Edward VI he was made Lord High Admiral, a post he held again during Queen Elizabeth's reign. He was created Earl of Lincoln in 1572 and died in 1585. Lord Clinton married as his third wife, *c.*1552, Lady Elizabeth Fitzgerald, celebrated in verse by the Earl of Surrey (Nos.32 and 36) as 'the fair Geraldine'.

55 Sir Nicholas Poyntz

55 Sir Nicholas Poyntz

Pink prepared paper. Black and coloured chalks, some strengthening with pen and black ink. 281 × 182 mm. Inscribed: *N Poines Knight*. Briquet 1050 (R.L.12234; Parker 34).

The son of Sir Anthony Poyntz (? 1486–1533) and the nephew of John Poyntz (No.51), Nicholas Poyntz was born in 1510 and married Joan, daughter of Thomas, Lord Berkeley. He was Sheriff of Gloucestershire in 1535 and from 1538 to 1544. He was knighted between 1531 and 33 and is shown in this drawing wearing his chain of knighthood. He was at court for the christening of Prince Edward in

56 Thomas, 2nd Baron Vaux

1537 and went to meet Anne of Cleves in 1540. In 1541 and 1542
Poyntz spent short periods in the Fleet prison for debt. He died in 1557.

There are various paintings which correspond with the drawing, of
which the finest is in the collection of the Earl of Harrowby, at Sandon
Hall; others are at Althorp, Ince Blundell and Ickworth.

56 Thomas, 2nd Baron Vaux

Pink prepared paper cut at the upper two corners. Black and coloured
chalks, watercolour with body-colour, some strengthening with black
ink applied with pen and brush. 277 × 292 mm. Annotated by the
artist: *silbe* (silver) twice, *rot* (red), *w.sam* (white velvet), *Gl* (gold),
karmin (carmine). The inscription has been cut so that only the last
two letters remain: *ux*. (R.L.12245; Parker 24).

Thomas, 2nd Lord Vaux of Harrowden, was born in 1510 and succeeded his father in 1523, by which time he had already married
Elizabeth Cheney (Nos.58 and 59). In 1527 he accompanied Wolsey

The Lord Vaux.

57 Thomas, 2nd Baron Vaux

to France, and returned there in 1532 as a member of King Henry VIII's embassy to meet the French King. In 1532 he was dubbed a Knight of the Bath. From January to August 1536 Vaux held his only official appointment, as Governor of the Isle of Jersey. After this date he appears to have spent his time mainly at home in Northamptonshire, for he disliked the movement towards Protestantism and remained a Roman Catholic. He died from the plague in October 1556.

Lord Vaux's poetry was published posthumously in various anthologies, including the influential *Tottel's Miscellany* of 1557. His poems are mainly elegiac and melancholy; they were popular with the Elizabethans, who appreciated his strong rhythms and often vivid imagery. He was related to several of those portrayed by Holbein: he was the brother-in-law of Sir Thomas Strange (No.72) and nephew

58 Elizabeth, Lady Vaux

of Sir Henry Guildford (Nos.12 and 13). Lady Vaux was a cousin of
the Earl of Northampton (No.53).

Vertue's copy of No.56 at Sudeley Castle shows the drawing with the
corners cut as at present.

57 Thomas, 2nd Baron Vaux

Pink prepared paper. Black and coloured chalks with some reinforcement in pen and black ink. 288 × 202 mm. Inscribed: *The Lord Vaux*.
(R.L.12246; Parker 30).

For biographical details see No.56.

Anonymous artist, after Holbein

58 Elizabeth, Lady Vaux

Panel. 380 × 286 mm (14 $\frac{15}{16}$ × 11 $\frac{1}{4}$ ins). (Millar, No.40).

Probably in the collection of King James II, this painting is a careful

95

The Lady Vaux.

59 Elizabeth, Lady Vaux

copy, perhaps made early in the seventeenth century, after a lost
original of *c.*1535, which was based on No.59. A smaller and possibly
better version is in the National Gallery, Prague (Ganz, *Paintings*, No.90,
Figs.23–24).

Elizabeth, the wife of Thomas, 2nd Baron Vaux (Nos.56 and 57),
was born between 1505 and 1509, the daughter of Sir Thomas Cheney,
an Esquire of the Body to King Henry VIII. She became a ward of
the 1st Baron Vaux in 1516 and was married to his son before May 1523.
Lady Vaux died shortly after her husband, on 20th November 1556,
probably also a victim of the plague.

59 Elizabeth, Lady Vaux

Pink prepared paper. Black and coloured chalks, with some rein-

96

60 Sir John Gage

forcement in black ink applied with pen and brush. Some white body-
colour heightening. The outlines gone over with metalpoint. 279 × 212
mm. Inscribed: *The Lady Vaux*. Briquet 1050 (R.L.12247; Parker 25).
For biographical notes see No.58. Much of the pen work and probably
the black wash on the head-dress appear to be retouching.

60 Sir John Gage

Pink prepared paper. Black and coloured chalks, with some ink
reinforcement applied with pen and brush. Metalpoint on gown. 394 ×
289 mm. Inscribed: *Gage*. Briquet 878 (R.L.12207; Parker 78).

Born in 1479, John Gage took part in the 1513 expedition to France

61 An Unknown Lady

and was subsequently made Governor of Guisnes and Comptroller of Calais. In 1528 he was appointed Vice-Chamberlain to the King, a post he held until 1540. In 1541 he was elected a Knight of the Garter. Sir John Gage was commander of the army against Scotland in 1542 and against France in 1544. He became Lord Chamberlain in 1553 and died in 1557. Gage remained an ardent Roman Catholic; in 1533 it was reported that he was 'more disposed to serve God than the world', but he continued in office. His wife Phillippa was a sister of Sir Henry Guildford (Nos.12 and 13).

The cap worn by Gage is of the same type as that worn by Sharington (No.65), where the brim is partly turned up.

This drawing has been extensively damaged; the work in chalk is much rubbed and the drawing has been insensitively reworked in wash by a later hand.

The Lady Ratclif.

62 Lady Ratcliffe

61 An Unknown Lady

Pink prepared paper. Black and coloured chalks, the outlines reinforced with pen and black ink. 274×201 mm. (R.L.12257; Parker 27).

62 Lady Ratcliffe

Pink prepared paper. Black and coloured chalks, some strengthening
in black ink with pen and brush, and some details of the jewelry added
in metalpoint. 299×200 mm. Annotated by the artist: *damast black*
(black damask) and *schwarz felbet* (black velvet). Inscribed: *The Lady
Ratclif.* (R.L.12236; Parker 19).

The identification of the sitter is problematical. It has been suggested
that she could be Mary Arundell, third wife of Robert Ratcliffe
(1483–1542), created Earl of Sussex in 1529. The marriage took place

63 An Unknown Lady

on 14th January 1537, but the style of the drawing would seem to date it before 1537; moreover, the Countess was known as 'my lady Sussex', as was the Earl's second wife, Margaret Stanley, whom he married in 1531.

Henry Ratcliffe, the son and heir of the Earl of Sussex, was born *c.*1506 and married Elizabeth Howard, the sister of the Duke of Norfolk, (No.37), before May 1524. If she is the lady here represented the drawing must date from before September 1534, when she died; her husband married again before 1538. On the grounds of the resemblance of this drawing to others of the Howard family (Nos.32–36), Parker concluded that Elizabeth Howard was most likely to be represented here; however, her proper title was Lady Fitzwalter, as the wife of the eldest son of the Earl of Sussex.

Lodge suggested that the sitter might be the wife of the 1st Earl's third son, Sir Humphrey Ratcliffe, who was Isabel Hervey. The date of their marriage is not known, but her title would have been Lady Ratcliffe, that inscribed on this drawing.

Among the details of jewelry executed in metalpoint on the left of the drawing Parker noted a reversed letter 'S', presumably standing for 'Sussex'. There seems no reason why the daughter-in-law of the house should not bear this initial herself.

Lady Ratcliffe's head-dress incorporates a hood, one of the ends of which is thrown up over the head while the other hangs down. If the hood were velvet a pin would be unnecessary because the velvet end would cling to the velvet covering the head. Similar head-dresses are worn by Lady Elyot (No.30), Lady Surrey (No.33) and many others depicted by Holbein, including Queen Jane Seymour (No.46).

63 An Unknown Lady

Pink prepared paper. Black chalk, partly stumped, and coloured chalks. Outlines reinforced with pen and black ink. 286 × 228 mm. Annotated by the artist: *S Sam* (? for *schwarz sammet*, black velvet), *Satin* and *S. Satin*. (R.L.12255, Parker 45).

It has been suggested that this drawing forms a pendant to No.52 in this exhibition.

64 Catherine, Duchess of Suffolk

Pink prepared paper. Black and coloured chalks. Some outlines reinforced with pen and black ink. 289 × 209 mm. Annotated by the artist: *rot* (red) and *damast* (damask). Inscribed: *The Dutchefs of Suffolk*. (R.L.12194; Parker 56).

The sitter is presumably Catherine, the fourth wife of Charles Brandon, 1st Duke of Suffolk, mother of Henry and Charles Brandon (Nos.85 and 86) and the step-mother of Lady Monteagle (No.20). She was born *c.*1519, the daughter of Baron Willoughby de Eresby and his Spanish wife, who was a lady-in-waiting to Queen Katherine of Aragon. She became a ward of the Duke of Suffolk, and was intended as a wife for his eldest son but, in September 1533, the Duke married her himself.

The career of the Duchess of Suffolk after the death of her elderly husband in 1544 was an adventurous and celebrated one. She married a fellow Protestant, Richard Bertie, *c.*1553, and in 1554, to escape persecution under Queen Mary, they left England with their children

64 Catherine, Duchess of Suffolk

and travelled across Europe to Poland; they returned in 1558. The Duchess died in 1580.

Doubts have been raised as to whether this drawing can really represent a girl as young as the Duchess while she was married to her first husband. In the collection of the Earl of Ancaster at Grimsthorpe Castle there is a miniature purporting to represent the Duchess of Suffolk; this is unrelated to Holbein's drawing, the sitter having somewhat different features.

65 Sir William Sharington

Pink prepared paper. Black and coloured chalks, partly stumped. 301 × 202 mm. Inscribed: *William Sharinton*, beneath which there appears to be a letter 'V', probably a mutilated 'K' for Knight (R.L.12241; Parker 75).

65 Sir William Sharington

Born *c*.1493, Sharington came to court in the service of Sir Francis
Bryan and was made a Page of the King's Robes. In 1540 he acquired
the dissolved Lacock Abbey in Wiltshire where he carried out
extensive rebuilding in the style of the French Renaissance. In 1541 he
was made Groom of the Privy Chamber. At the time of the Coronation
of King Edward VI in 1547, Sharington was made a Knight of the
Bath. The previous year he had been appointed Vice-Treasurer of the
Mint at Bristol. In this position he enriched himself by more than ten
thousand pounds through a variety of fraudulent practices. Eventually
in *c*.1549 he was arrested and imprisoned in the Tower on a charge of
fraud but he was pardoned and in 1552 served as Sheriff of Wiltshire.
Sharington died in 1553.

Brooke Ld Cobham.

66 George Brooke, 9th Baron Cobham

66 George Brooke, 9th Baron Cobham

Pink prepared paper. Black chalk, partly stumped, red chalk, partly stumped, and coloured chalks. Reinforced in pen and black ink, also metalpoint. 288 × 203 mm. Inscribed: *Brooke Ld Cobham.* (R.L.12195; Parker 53).

George Brooke was born *c.*1497, knighted in 1523 and succeeded his father as 9th Lord Cobham in 1529. He was frequently summoned to Councils by the King, and was among those who officiated at the trial of Queen Anne Boleyn in 1536. He was an eager supporter of the King's new religious policies. In 1544, Cobham was made Deputy of

Phillip Hobbie Knight

67 Sir Philip Hoby

Calais and two years later he was Lieutenant General in the Scottish campaign. He was elected a Knight of the Garter in 1549 and, as a Protestant, was involved in the younger Wyatt's rebellion against Queen Mary. He was pardoned and died in 1559. Lord Cobham's sister was married to the poet Wyatt (Nos.79 and 80), and his daughter to the Marquis of Northampton (No.53).

No convincing explanation has been put forward as to why Lord Cobham and Sir Charles Wingfield (No.41) are depicted by Holbein in varying states of undress, and since no paintings connected with these two drawings survive, it is impossible to say whether Holbein intended ultimately to show the sitters in more formal dress or not.

The Lady Hobbei.

68 Elizabeth, Lady Hoby

67 Sir Philip Hoby

Pink prepared paper. Black and coloured chalks. 300 × 233 mm. Inscribed: *Phillip Hobbie Knight*. Briquet 8653 (R.L.12210; Parker 50).

Sir Philip Hoby was continually employed by King Henry VIII as a diplomat. He was born in 1500 and his first important mission was as envoy to the courts of Spain and Portugal from 1535 to 1536. During 1538 he travelled abroad with Holbein on three occasions so that the latter could portray those whom the King sought to marry: in March they visited Brussels to take the portrait of Christina, Duchess of Milan (now in the National Gallery, London), in June, Le Havre, and in August, Nancy and Joinville. Hoby was made a Groom of the Privy Chamber in the same year, and a Gentleman Usher in 1539. Like others who sat to Holbein, Hoby was a Protestant and a member of Crom-

The Lady Buts.

69 Margaret, Lady Butts

well's faction, and yet he, like them (*e.g.* Nos.23, 40 and 75), survived Cromwell's fall in 1540. Sir Philip was knighted in 1544. Under King Edward VI he carried out further diplomatic embassies and died in 1558. He was known as an amiable and cultured man and was a friend of Titian and Pietro Aretino. Hoby married Elizabeth Stonor (No.68) *c.*1539 and the two drawings may well have been done at about this time.

68 Elizabeth, Lady Hoby

Pink prepared paper. Black and coloured chalks. The outlines reinforced in ink applied with pen and brush. 275 × 201 mm. Inscribed: *The Lady Hobbei.* Briquet 8653 (R.L. 12211; Parker 51).

The sitter was the daughter of Sir Walter Stonor, and was born *c.*1500.

70 An Unknown Lady

She married Sir Philip Hoby (No.67) as her third husband before 1540; her second husband, Sir Walter Walsh, Privy Chamberlain to King Henry VIII, died in 1538. Lady Hoby died in 1560. Like Sir Philip, she embraced the Protestant cause and, along with Lady Butts (No.69), she was a member of the circle around Queen Catherine Parr.

The drawing is very rubbed and has been heavily reinforced with pen and brush by a later hand.

69 Margaret, Lady Butts

Pink prepared paper. Black and coloured chalks. Reinforced with black ink applied with pen and brush. Extensive use of metalpoint over the entire drawing. 377 × 272 mm. Inscribed: *The Lady Buts*. (R.L.12264; Parker 67).

The sitter was the daughter of John Bacon of Cambridgeshire and the wife of Sir William Butts, Physician to King Henry VIII. In 1532

71 Sir Thomas Parry

she is recorded as a lady-in-waiting to Princess Mary and her husband was also attendant on the Princess. Lady Butts was later recorded as a Protestant and like Lady Hoby (No.68) she was closely linked with Queen Catherine Parr.

There is a painted portrait of Lady Butts after this drawing in the Isabella Stewart Gardner Museum, Boston, where Holbein's companion portrait of her husband also hangs (Ganz, *Paintings*, Nos.125 and 124, pls.166 and 165), but for the latter no drawing survives. The sitter's age is given as fifty-seven on the Boston picture.

This drawing exemplifies the rather flat style usually associated with the latter stages of Holbein's career.

70 An Unknown Lady

Pink prepared paper. Black chalk, partly stumped, and coloured chalks, 286 × 217 mm. Annotated by the artist: *damast sh* (black damask). Close to Briquet 1457 (R.L.12256; Parker 48).

Tho: Strange Knight.

72 Sir Thomas Strange

71 Sir Thomas Parry

Pink prepared paper. Black and coloured chalks. Some outlines reinforced in pen and black ink. 256 × 184 mm. Inscribed: *Thomas Parrie.*
(R.L.12232; Parker 81).

Parry was a Welshman and one of Cromwell's agents in the period of
the Dissolution of the Monasteries. During Queen Mary's reign, he
attended Princess Elizabeth and on the latter's succession in 1558 he
was knighted and made a Privy Councillor and Comptroller of the
Household. The following year Parry became Master of the Court of
Wards and Liveries. He died in 1560.

At the top of the drawing Holbein has made a separate sketch for
the hat-badge, which is very similar to that on the painted portrait
of Sir Richard Southwell in the Uffizi (Ganz, *Paintings*, No.88, pl.131).

Francis Russel E: of Bedford *some time after*

73 Francis Russell, 2nd Earl of Bedford

72 Sir Thomas Strange

Pink prepared paper. Black chalk, partly stumped, and white and coloured chalks. 243 × 210 mm. Inscribed: *Tho: Strange Knight* (R.L.12244; Parker 43).

Sir Thomas Strange or Lestrange of Hunstanton Hall in Norfolk was born in 1494. He was an Esquire of the Body to King Henry VIII and was present at the Field of the Cloth of Gold in 1520. He was knighted in 1529. Sir Thomas was Sheriff of Norfolk in 1532, and after this date was permanently resident in Norfolk where, in 1536, he participated in the inquiry into the revenues of Walsingham Abbey, along with Sir Richard Southwell (No.23). He was married to Anne, sister of Lord Vaux (Nos.56 and 57), and died on 16th January 1545.

The painted portrait by Holbein after this drawing is in an American private collection (Ganz, *Paintings*, No.89, pl.132).

73 Francis Russell, 2nd Earl of Bedford

Pink prepared paper. Black and coloured chalks. Outlines reinforced in pen and grey/brown ink. 241 × 179 mm. Annotated by the artist: *rot damast* (red damask). Inscribed: *Francis Russel E: of Bedford some time after*, the last three words being in a different script. Close to Briquet 8653 (R.L.12240; Parker 70).

Francis Russell, the son of John Russell, 1st Earl of Bedford (No.27), was born *c.*1527 and educated at Cambridge. He accompanied his father to France in 1544 and was dubbed a Knight of the Bath on the accession of King Edward VI. As a Protestant he was imprisoned when Mary became Queen, and after succeeding his father as 2nd Earl of Bedford in 1555 he travelled to Italy. While abroad he became a lifelong friend of members of the Protestant community at Zürich. In 1557 he returned to England, and under Queen Elizabeth became a Privy Councillor; he was also a patron of colleges at both Oxford and Cambridge. Bedford was killed in a skirmish on the Scottish border on 28th July 1585.

Very little of Holbein's original drawing remains: the chalk is severely rubbed and the penwork is by another hand.

74 Edward, Prince of Wales

Pink prepared paper. Black and coloured chalks. Reinforced in ink applied with pen or brush. 262 × 223 mm. Inscribed: *Edward Prince*. (R.L.12200; Parker 46).

The future King Edward VI, the son of King Henry VIII and his third wife, Queen Jane Seymour (No.46), was born at Hampton Court on 12th October 1537. He had his own household from 1539, and in 1544 Sir John Cheke, who was apparently responsible for the original identifications of all the Holbein portrait drawings at Windsor, was appointed the Prince's tutor. Edward was educated in the classics and the Bible, modern languages and music, along with chosen noble schoolmates including Henry and Charles Brandon (Nos.85 and 86).

On 21st January 1547 Edward succeeded his father as King. The Earl of Hertford, later Duke of Somerset, was appointed Lord Protector, and after his execution in 1552 the Earl of Northumberland succeeded him. During King Edward's reign the country saw a form of Protestantism come to the fore which was far more extreme than anything countenanced by Henry VIII, and Edward was praised by foreign Reformers for his 'holy disposition'. Of a learned and serious

Edward Prince.

74 Edward, Prince of Wales

cast of mind, King Edward was physically weak throughout his short life; he died at the age of fifteen on 6th July 1553.

Numerous portraits were produced of Edward, both as Prince and King, but Holbein's drawing of him as a very young child is the earliest extant likeness (see Strong, NPG, pp.57–94). This drawing is a study for Holbein's portrait of Prince Edward, now in the National Gallery, Washington (Ganz, *Paintings*, No.105, pl.146). This was possibly the picture of Edward presented to the King by Holbein on 1st January 1539.

No.74 is one of the most rubbed drawings in the Windsor series, some of the outlines being hardly perceptible, whilst others have been reinforced by another hand.

75 Richard, 1st Baron Rich

75 Richard, 1st Baron Rich

Pink prepared paper. Black and coloured chalks, some reinforcing with pen and black ink. 320 × 261 mm. Inscribed: *Rich Ld Chancelor*. Briquet 11387 (R.L.12238; Parker 80).

Probably born in 1496, Rich became Solicitor-General in 1533 and M.P. for Essex in 1536. He was Chancellor of Augmentations from 1536–44. Rich was raised to the peerage in 1548, and from 1548–51 served as Lord Chancellor. He founded Felstead Grammar School in Essex in 1564 and died three years later. Rich rose as a protégé of Cromwell. He was ambitious and totally unscrupulous. Together with Sir Thomas Audley (probably the husband of Lady Audley, Nos.44

76 Elizabeth, Lady Rich

and 83), he was responsible for the interrogation of Sir Thomas More (Nos.1 and 2) on the subject of the King's Supremacy, whilst More was confined in the Tower. It was largely on Rich's perjured evidence that Sir Thomas was convicted and thereafter condemned to death.

The drawing is very rubbed but appears to be from Holbein's hand and to have been a pendant to the drawing of Lady Rich (No.76).

76 Elizabeth, Lady Rich

Pink prepared paper. Black and coloured chalks. Some reinforcing with pen and black ink. 374 × 200 mm. Annotated in the artist's hand: *Damast* (damask) and *samet* (velvet). Inscribed twice: *The Lady Rich.*

(once at the top left, secondly, very faintly at the level of the sitter's right shoulder). Briquet 11387 (R.L.12271; Parker 55).

The sitter was the daughter of William Jenks, a wealthy London spice merchant. She married Richard, 1st Baron Rich (No.75) in 1535, and died in 1558, having produced fifteen children.

The drawing was used for a painting, known in a later version now in the Metropolitan Museum, New York (Ganz, *Paintings*, No.117, pl.156). There Lady Rich wears a medallion of an unidentifiable subject, which does not appear in the drawing.

77 John Colet

Pink prepared paper. Black and coloured chalks and some reinforcing with point of brush and ink. Metalpoint in the vestments. 267 × 202 mm. Inscribed: *Iohn Colet Dean of St Paul's*. Briquet 11391 (RL.12199; Parker 59).

John Colet was born *c.*1467, the son of a Lord Mayor of London. He studied at Oxford and was ordained in 1498. From 1497 to 1503 he gave an important series of lectures at Oxford on the New Testament, criticising the Church and insisting on fidelity to the overt meaning of Biblical texts. During this time he met Erasmus (Nos.5 and 6) and after he settled in London in 1504 as Dean of St Paul's, he became a close friend of Sir Thomas More (Nos.1 and 2). In 1509 Colet founded St Paul's School. Although he died in 1519, before Holbein's first visit to England, it has been shown that Holbein made this drawing after a bust of the sitter made by the Italian sculptor, Pietro Torrigiano, as part of Colet's tomb in St Paul's (F. Grossmann, 'Holbein, Torrigiano and Portraits of Dean Colet', *Journal of the Warburg and Courtauld Institutes*, XIII, 1950, pp.202–236). At the same time it was suggested that this posthumous portrait drawing was made for Sir Thomas More, and that it was executed early in Holbein's second visit to England, certainly before 1535. More recently it has been proposed that No.77 dates from the first visit (see NPG, *More*, No.11), but the detailed work in ink on pink priming seems to set it apart from the other known drawings from this time, which are chiefly in chalk on unprepared paper.

The drawing is an outstanding example of Holbein's skilful use of ink applied with the point of the brush and it closely follows the contemporary cast of Torrigiano's bust belonging to St Paul's School, even to the extent that the base of the sculpture is visible in the lower outlines of the drawing. The original carving in Old St Paul's was destroyed during the Great Fire of 1666.

It is not the only example of Holbein's ability to invest a drawing of a

77 John Colet

piece of sculpture with the wholly convincing appearance of a drawing from life. Compare, for instance, the two drawings in Basel of the life-sized sepulchral effigies of Jean, duc de Berri and his wife from Bourges Cathedral, dating from Holbein's visit to France in 1524 (Ganz, *Drawings*, Nos. 13 and 12).

78 Philip Melanchthon (?)

Pink prepared paper. Black and coloured chalks, the brown chalk stumped. Some reinforcing with ink and point of brush 283 × 232 mm. Inscribed: *Phil: Melanchton*. Close to Briquet 1457 (R.L. 12221; Parker 68).

The identifying inscription on this drawing is problematic. Philip Melanchthon (1497–1560) was a German Reformer and a Professor of

Phil: Melanchton.

78 Philip Melanchthon (?)

Greek and Theology; he drafted the Lutheran Augsburg Confession of
1530. Holbein portrayed Melanchthon in *c*.1530 in a small painted
roundel now in Hanover (Ganz, *Paintings*, No.53, pl.94). However,
the painting is not directly related to this drawing, and Melanchthon
is not known ever to have come to England. Nevertheless, there are
perhaps sufficient similarities between the sitter in this drawing and
Melanchthon as portrayed by Holbein in the painting for the inscription
not to be dismissed out of hand.

The drawing is extremely rubbed and has been retouched by a
later hand.

Tho: Wiatt Knight.

79 Sir Thomas Wyatt

Sir Thomas Wyatt

Pink prepared paper. Black and coloured chalks. Reinforcement in
ink applied with pen and brush. 371 × 270 mm. Inscribed: *Tho: Wiatt
Knight*. (R.L.12250; Parker 64).

The son of Sir Henry Wyatt, the King's Treasurer (himself portrayed
by Holbein in a picture now in the Louvre; Ganz *Paintings*, No.50,
pl.87), Thomas Wyatt was born *c*.1503. He studied at Cambridge and in
1524 was appointed Clerk of the King's Jewels. In 1527 he was sent on
a diplomatic mission to Italy with John Russell, Earl of Bedford
(No.27). When Queen Anne Boleyn was accused of adultery in 1536
Wyatt was sent to the Tower for he had probably been her lover

Sr Tho: Wiat Kt.

80 Sir Thomas Wyatt

before she became Queen, but he was released shortly afterwards. In later
years he was sent on various important missions, to Spain in 1537 and to
the Low Countries in 1540. In the latter year he was again imprisoned
in the Tower and then in 1541 was set free. In 1542, Wyatt was returned
to Parliament but in October of that year he died very suddenly from a
fever. In 1520 he had married Elizabeth Brooke, the sister of Lord
Cobham (No.66), but they later separated (see No.48).

Sir Thomas Wyatt is probably the best known literary figure of
King Henry VIII's reign. Like the Earl of Surrey (Nos.32 and 36)
he imitated Petrarch's sonnets, but he also wrote less formal lyrics,

some of which were intended to be sung to the accompaniment of a lute. In 1542, Leland's elegy on Wyatt's death was published with a roundel woodcut portrait of Wyatt in profile, but this is not connected with the drawing exhibited here (for Wyatt's iconography see Strong, NPG, pp.338–39).

This drawing and its companion (No.80) illustrate a problem which sometimes arises with drawings of this type, though rarely with Holbein. They are almost identical and the question is: are both original? are both copies of a lost original? or is one an original and one a copy and if so, which is which? The problem is made the more difficult by the fact that the drawings have been badly rubbed and retouched. No.80 more than No.79.

Sir Karl Parker concluded that No.79 was the original and No.80 a copy, and wrote: 'The difference in quality between the two drawings is nevertheless marked, the superiority of [No.79] being manifest at first sight', but the reverse has also been maintained. Unfortunately so little is left visible of the original work in No.80 that it is almost impossible to make a judgement, positive or negative. The artist who reworked it with a pen has done his work so thoroughly that only the end of the beard remains – and that so worn as to be almost without character. Worse, he seems to have redrawn the contour of the sitter's left cheek wrongly, distorting the line so that one half of the face appears narrower than the other. In No.79 the general effect is un-questionably better on first impression, but the drawing of the features and of the beard, which has been less heavily retouched than the moustache, has a mechanical quality which, it can be argued, is not to be found in originals by Holbein.

All these opinions are certainly subjective and any judgement must depend on individual reactions to the two drawings. Sir Karl Parker suggested, very tentatively, that No.80 might be a copy by Federico Zuccaro, who is known to have made copies of designs by Holbein, but the condition of the drawing is so bad that any such attribution is difficult to substantiate.

80 Sir Thomas Wyatt

Pink prepared paper. Black and coloured chalks. Extensive rein-forcing in black ink applied with pen and brush. 372 × 274 mm. Inscribed: Sr Tho: $Wiat$ K^t. Close to Briquet 11219 (R.L.12251; Parker 65).

For biographical and technical details see the companion drawing of Wyatt (No.79).

81 *Remigius van Leemput after Holbein* Henry VIII, Jane Seymour, Henry VII and Elizabeth of York

Remigius van Leemput (d.1675)

81 Henry VII, Elizabeth of York, Henry VIII and Jane Seymour

Canvas. 889×987 mm (35×38⅞ ins). Inscribed, signed and dated at the base of the plinth:
PROTOTYPVM IVSTÆ MAGNITVDINIS IPSO OPERE TECTORIO/FECIT HOLBENIVS IVBENTE HENRICO VIII./ ECTYPVS A REMIGIO VAN LEEMPVT BREVIORI TABELLA/ DESCRIBI VOLVIT CAROLVS II. M.B. F.E.H.R./. Aº DNI. MDCLXVII.
(Holbein made the original, life size, on the wall, at the command of Henry VIII. Charles II, K(ing) (of) G(reat) B(ritain) F(rance) (and) I(reland), ordered a copy to be made in a smaller picture by Remigius van Leemput. In the year of Our Lord 1667.) Inscribed above:
SI IVV AT HEROVM CLARAS VIDISSE FIGVRAS,
SPECTA HAS, MAIORES NVLLA TABELLA TVLIT.
CERTAMEN MAGNVM, LIS, QVÆSTIO MAGNA PATERNE,
FILIVS AN VINCAT. VICIT. VTERQVE QVIDEM.

ISTE SVOS HOSTES, PATRIÆQVE INCENDIA SÆPE
SVSTVLIT, ET PACEM CIVIBVS VSQVE DEDIT.
FILIVS AD MAIORA QVIDEM PROGNATVS AB ARIS
SVBMOVET INDIGNOSI SVBSTITVITQVE PROBOS.
CERTÆ, VIRTVTI, PAPARVM AVDACIA CESSIT,
HENRICO OCTAVO SCEPTRA GERENTE MANV
REDDITA RELIGIO EST, ISTO REGNANTE DEIQVE
DOGMATA CEPERVNT ESSE IN HONORE SVO.

(If it pleases you to see the images of great heroes, look on these: no picture figures greater. Great controversy, contention and great doubt arise whether father or son be supreme. Each was victorious indeed. The father many times endured the assaults of his enemies and the conflagration of his country, and brought peace everywhere to its citizens.

The son born to greater things, removed the unworthy from their altars and replaced them by upright men. The arrogance of the Popes yielded to proven virtue, while Henry VIII held the sceptre true religion was restored and during his reign the decrees of God began to be honoured.)   (Millar, No.216)

This copy by Leemput, after Holbein's 1537 mural in the Privy Chamber at Whitehall Palace, appears to have cost £150. It seems that Leemput made slight modifications from the source, which was eventually destroyed in the fire at Whitehall on 4th January 1698: 'endeavours were us'd to remove that part of the Wall on which these Pictures were painted, but all prov'd ineffectual'.

Dr Roy Strong (*Henry VIII*, pp.34–58) suggests that the wall painting was on the upper half of the wall of the Privy Chamber, above the chair of state, but his reconstruction (*op. cit.*, p.53) shows that this would have involved quite a violent change of perspective between the actual space and that painted by Holbein. The perspective within the wall-painting, to judge from the surviving cartoon in the National Portrait Gallery and from Leemput's copy, was in no way different from what was normal in a free-standing, full-length portrait, and the design would have been seen more naturally, it may be suggested, if it were only slightly raised above floor level. Dr Strong makes a further suggestion that the central altar-like structure, with the important Latin verses, was an invention of Leemput to occupy a space which had been previously filled by a window. However, there has recently come to light an account, still unpublished, of a visit to London by a young German in 1600. He visited Whitehall Palace, apparently saw the wall-painting, and recorded the verses immediately after his reference to it (information kindly supplied by Mr G. W. Groos). If the verses were

82 *Anonymous artist, after Holbein* King Henry VIII

inscribed on and referred to the wall-painting, the use of the word 'TABELLA' would have been unusual, as Dr Strong states, since it would normally refer to a small picture, not a wall painting; but the verses do not record a seventeenth century gloss upon the mural or on its significance.

Anonymous artist, after Holbein

82 King Henry VIII

Panel. 997 × 743 mm (39¼ × 29¼ ins). (Millar, No.34).

This picture is not apparently recorded in the Royal Collection before the reign of King George III. It is an early derivation, at three-quarter-length, from the figure of the King in Holbein's wall-painting (1537) in the Privy Chamber at Whitehall. A large number of derivations (including several at full-length) are recorded; in all of them (as in Leemput's small copy, No.81) the head of the King is seen more frontally than in the original cartoon (now in the National Portrait Gallery; Strong, NPG, No.4027). If, indeed, Leemput's is a faithful copy, considerable modifications to the figure of the King were made between cartoon and mural in the details of the costume and in the outline of the King's shoulders. In this painting there are many small variations in the costume from the principal versions of the type.

83

83 **Elizabeth, Lady Audley** (*Colour plate VI*)

Watercolour on vellum laid on to a playing card. Circular, diam. 57 mm (2½ ins).

There is apparently no certain reference to this miniature being in the Royal Collection before it is mentioned by Woltmann (*Holbein und seine Zeit*, Leipzig, 1866, vol. II, p.248) and included in a list, drawn up in 1870, of miniatures in the Royal Library. It may tentatively be assumed that it was acquired by Queen Victoria. The sitter's identity is based on a comparison with the drawing (No.44); both the drawing and the miniature are datable *c*.1540.

Holbein's *œuvre* as a miniaturist has not been clearly defined, but there has been general agreement that the four miniatures in the Royal Collection (Nos.83–86) constitute a very important part of an undisputed basis on which it could be constructed (see A. B. Chamberlain, *Hans Holbein the Younger*, London, 1913, vol.II, pp.217–42; B. S. Long, *British Miniaturists*, 1929, p.214; Graham Reynolds, *English Portrait Miniatures*, 1952, p.4, and his invaluable notes on the miniatures in the Royal Collection). In 1977 a detailed examination of these four miniatures was carried out at the Victoria and Albert Museum by Mr J. Murrell, together with the two attributed to Holbein in the Duke of Buccleuch's collection and the two in the Museum's own collection. It was generally agreed that the eight miniatures were from the same hand. The jewelry in them was painted in the same manner, and in Nos.85 and 86 the hands had been corrected by the artist himself.

Technical similarities with miniatures now attributed to Lucas Horenbout (*e.g.* Nos.89 and 90) tend to confirm that Holbein, who apparently took up miniature painting only after he had come to London, was influenced by him in the technical aspects of the art; and the juxtaposition in the Queen's Gallery on this occasion of the four Holbeins and four miniatures by Hilliard (Nos.91–94) illuminates Hilliard's famous tribute to the older painter: 'Holbean's maner of limning I have ever imitated and howld it for the best'.

84

84 An Unknown Lady (*Colour plate VII*)

Watercolour on vellum laid on to playing card. Circular, diam. 64 mm (2½ ins).

Almost certainly acquired by Queen Victoria, the miniature was described from the early 1840s as a portrait of Catherine Howard, although P. Fraser Tytler in his notes on some of the Queen's miniatures (*c.*1845) was doubtful of this identity, chiefly because the sitter did not seem to resemble the lady in the drawing at Windsor alleged to represent Catherine Howard (Parker 62). There is, however, no portrait which can be regarded as a certain likeness of her. Most writers on Holbein have noted the similarity between the sitter in this miniature and in the painting in Toledo, Ohio (Ganz, *Paintings*, No.118, pl.157). Of the two versions of this miniature, which was probably painted *c*.1540, that in the Royal Collection was perhaps the one painted *ad vivum*. The other version is in the collection of the Duke of Buccleuch; this was first stated to represent Catherine Howard early in the eighteenth century (Strong, NPG, p.44).

85

85 Henry Brandon, 2nd Duke of Suffolk *(Colour plate VIII)*

Watercolour on vellum laid on to playing card. Circular, diam. 57 mm (2¼ ins). Inscribed: *ETATIS. SVÆ.5.6.SEPDEM.|ANNO|1535.*

For biographical details see the companion miniature, No.86. The inscription apparently records the sitter's age at the time of painting and his date of birth.

86 Charles Brandon, 3rd Duke of Suffolk *(Colour plate IX)*

Watercolour on vellum laid on to playing card. Circular, diam. 57 mm (2¼ ins). Inscribed: *ANN|1541|.ETATIS SVÆ 3|.10.MARCI.*

The two portraits of the Brandon boys were given to King Charles I by Sir Henry Fanshaw; they were placed with the other miniatures in the King's collection, which were then housed in the Cabinet Room at Whitehall, and they were stated to have been 'Don by Hanc Holben'.

Henry and Charles Brandon were the sons of Charles Brandon, 1st Duke of Suffolk (died 1545) and his fourth wife, Catherine, Duchess of Suffolk (No.64). Henry Brandon (born 1535) was educated with the young Prince Edward (No.75) and at his Coronation in 1547 he carried the Orb; both Henry and Charles (*b*.1537/8) were made Knights of the Bath on the day of the Coronation. Henry was described as 'animosus, fortis, robustus, et ad militarem disciplinam, non factus,

86 Charles Brandon,
3rd Duke of Suffolk

sed natus', while his younger brother Charles was 'non robustus . . . .
sed elegans'. In 1551 the two boys died of the sweating sickness within
half an hour of each other, and at the death of Charles the Dukedom of
Suffolk became extinct. The brothers were renowned for their learning
(both were at St John's College, Cambridge) and their untimely death
made a deep impression on their contemporaries.

In contrast to that on No.85, the inscription on No.86 apparently
records the sitter's age and the date on which the miniature was
executed (10th March 1541).

87

87 Hat Jewel (c.1540)

Of gold enamelled in high relief with St George and the Dragon and
the kneeling Princess. The back is decorated with a geometric pattern
in gold on a green enamel ground. Circular, diam. 41 mm (1⅝ ins).

This jewel dates from c.1540 and may have been made in South
Germany. It is traditionally said to have been presented by the
Emperor Maximilian, who reigned from 1493 to 1519, to King Henry
VIII, but the dating suggested above does not support this tradition.

88 Solomon and the Queen of Sheba

88 Solomon and the Queen of Sheba *(Colour plate and detail on front cover)*

On vellum. Pen and brush work in various colours, some watercolour, some body-colour. 227 × 183 mm. Inscribed: *REGINA SABA* (the Queen of Sheba) in foreground; and on either side of the throne: *BEATI VIRI TVI . . . . . . ET BEATI SERVI HI TVI/QVI ASSISTANT CORAM TE . . . . . OMNITPE ET AVDIVNT/ SAPIENTIAM TVAM;* on the curtain behind Solomon: *SIT DOMINVS DEVS BENEDICTVS,/CVI COMPLACIT IN TE, UT PONERET TE/SVPER THRONVM, VT ESSES REX/ (CONSTITUTVS) DOMINO DEO TVO.* (A translation of the inscription, which is based on II Chronicles 9, v.7–8, is as follows: Happy are thy men and happy are these thy servants, who stand in thy presence, and hear thy wisdom. Blessed be the Lord thy God, who delighted in thee, to set thee upon his throne, to be king (elected) by the Lord thy God); and on the steps of the throne, *VICISTI FAMAM VIRTVTIBVS* (By your virtues you have exceeded your reputation). (R.L.12188; Parker Frontispiece).

This exquisite miniature painting is first recorded in the collection of the Earl of Arundel, where it was engraved by Hollar in 1642 (Parthey 74) and listed in the inventory of 1654. By 1743 it had passed into the Royal Collection.

The subject is King Solomon's meeting with the Queen of Sheba and her train (I Kings 10, v.1–13 and II Chronicles 9, v.1–13). The figure of Solomon is a portrait of King Henry VIII, the first known example of Solomon being given a contemporary likeness in such a representation.

The style of the miniature must date it early in Holbein's second visit to England; the Italianate foreground figures in particular are very close to Holbein's design for the Hanseatic 'Triumph of Riches' (see Ganz, *Paintings*, No.177). It has been said that it must date from after 8th May 1535, when Stow states that King Henry decreed beards were to be worn (see Parker, p.24), but as the King is already documented with a beard in 1531 (see Strong, NPG, p.157) and is shown wearing one in the miniature attributed to Horenbout of *c*.1525 (No. 90), and there is no other witness of this decree, great reliance cannot be put upon it. Holbein portrayed the King for the frontispiece of the Coverdale Bible in 1535 and one of these two representations must be the first extant portrait of him that Holbein made.

The inscription over the King's head may well allude to the events leading up to Henry VIII's assumption of the role of Supreme Head of the Church in 1534; the text implies that Henry VIII, like Solomon, is answerable only to God. The Queen of Sheba was traditionally a type of the Church, and it is possible that this meaning is implicit here, so that King Henry is shown receiving the homage of the Church. The text incorporated in the inscription is not the text of the Vulgate which was traditionally used in the sixteenth century, and it may be for this reason that the word 'CONSTITUTUS' has been bracketed.

This miniature, delicate in execution and enriched with gold, is the type of object which was presented to Henry VIII as a New Year's gift, although it is not specifically recorded as such. The quality and high degree of finish makes it seem unlikely that Holbein intended to transpose the Solomon and the Queen of Sheba design into a wall painting, as has been suggested.

89

Attributed to Lucas Horenbout (d.1544)

89 King Henry VIII

Watercolour on vellum. Circular, diam. 40 mm ($1\frac{9}{16}$ ins). Inscribed: *REX.|.HENRICVS.OCT|AVVS.*

Lucas Horenbout, whose style had been formed in the Flemish school (he became a member of the painters' guild in Ghent in 1512), had come to England before 1528 and there entered the King's service. He is assumed to have been the 'master Lukas' who had given Holbein instruction in the art of miniature painting, and to have been responsible for a small group of miniatures, painted in a distinctively Flemish style at the early Tudor court, of which the portraits of the King himself are the nucleus (see Graham Reynolds's detailed notes on miniatures in the Royal Collection, and his *Connoisseur Guide, Tudor Period* (1956), pp.128–29; also Erna Auerbach, *Nicholas Hilliard* (1961), pp.49–51).

The miniatures of the King now associated with Horenbout are those which were presented to King Charles I by the 2nd Earl of Suffolk. Two are still in the Royal Collection (Nos.89 and 90); another, formerly in the Buccleuch collection, is now in the Fitzwilliam Museum, Cambridge (there is a copy, probably by G. P. Harding, in the Royal Library); the fourth, still in the Buccleuch collection, has on the back the label applied by Abraham van der Doort, who was Surveyor of Charles I's pictures. The latter is very close in type to No.89 and gives the King's age as thirty-five, as does the version in the Fitzwilliam and also No.90 (which, however, shows him bearded). The miniatures are therefore datable *c.*1525.

90

Attributed to Lucas Horenbout (d.1544)

90 King Henry VIII

Watercolour on vellum. Circular, diam. 47 mm (1⅞ ins). Inscribed:
:H.R./.VIII:/AN̊.ETATIS./.XXXV̊:.

See No.89. This is a bearded variant of the type associated with
Horenbout and is datable from the inscription c.1525.

91

Nicholas Hilliard (1547–1619)

91 King Henry VIII

Watercolour on vellum, laid on to playing card. Circular, diam. 31 mm
(1 7/32 ins). Inscribed: .1536.Ætatis suæ.46.

This portrait is ultimately a derivation from the image of the King
painted by Holbein on the wall of the Privy Chamber (see No.81),
but the date given on the inscription is the year before that recorded
originally on the mural.

The four miniatures by Hilliard here exhibited (Nos.91–94) were
originally set 'in severall Cases one over another' in a golden jewel on
which were enamelled a representation of the battle of Bosworth Field,
and the red and white roses joined together. The jewel had been given
to King Charles I by Hilliard's son, Lawrence, through the mediation

of the 3rd Earl of Pembroke. The four portraits were copied by
Hilliard from existing likenesses (see Erna Auerbach, *Nicholas Hilliard,*
1961, pp.151, 311–12). Mr J. Murrell has pointed out that the four
miniatures are close in style to one in the Victoria and Albert Museum
(P25–1942) which is dated 1559 and is also a copy from an earlier work.

92

Nicholas Hilliard (1547–1619)

92 Queen Jane Seymour

Watercolour on vellum, laid on to card. Circular, diam. 31 mm
(1 $\frac{7}{32}$ ins). Inscribed: *Año Dñi. 1536. Ætatis suæ. 27.*

See No.91. The likeness is derived from Holbein's type of *c*.1536
(see No.46).

93

Nicholas Hilliard (1547–1619)

93 King Henry VII

Watercolour on vellum, laid on to card. Circular, diam. 32·5 mm
(1 $\frac{9}{32}$ ins). Inscribed: *Año Dñi: 1509: Ætatis Suæ. 54.*

See No.91. The portrait of King Henry VII is based on a type of which
a good version is in the Society of Antiquaries (Strong, NPG, vol.I,
p.151; vol.II, pl.293). The inscription records the age of the King
in the year of his death.

94

Nicholas Hilliard (1547–1619)

94 King Edward VI

Watercolour on vellum, laid on to card. Circular, diam. 32 mm (1¼ ins). Inscribed: *Ætatis suæ 14 Regni. 6.*

See No.91. The prototype is the portrait of the young King attributed to Guillim Stretes or Scrots, of which the most important version is the full-length at Hampton Court. The type may have originated in 1550 and at least one of the many versions and derivations is dated 29th September 1550 (see Millar, No.49).

95

95 Cameo of King Henry VIII and Prince Edward (c.1540)

Oval sardonyx of three strata (dark brown, bluish white and light brown). On the reverse is an unfinished intaglio, following roughly the same outlines. Height 58 mm (2 $\frac{5}{16}$ ins.), width 80 mm (3⅛ ins).

In 1763 this cameo was seen by Horace Walpole in a cabinet at Kensington Palace. He included it in a list of pictures and curiosities dated 2nd June 1763 which he added in manuscript to his copy of Bathoe's edition of *King James II's Catalogue,* published in 1758. The cameo together with other curiosities was delivered to King George III on 22nd March 1764 (Royal Archives, Geo. Addl. MSS. 16, 27–28).

There are several cameos very similar to Nos.95 and 96 in the collection of the Duke of Devonshire at Chatsworth; one representing Prince Edward is almost a replica of his image in No.95.

96

96 Cameo of King Henry VIII (c.1540)

Circular sardonyx of three strata (dark brown, white and light brown), diam. 40 mm ($1 \frac{9}{16}$ ins.).

97 Armour of King Henry VIII (c.1540)

Complete armour made up of portions of one or more suits with parts for the field and tilt. Bright steel with sunk borders etched and gilt with a variety of designs. Overall height 183 cm (72 ins).

The armour was made in the Royal Armouries at Greenwich which were established by King Henry VIII in 1517. Alterations for growth in both the thighs and body suggest that this may be the armour recorded at Greenwich in the custody of Sir Thomas Pastone in 1547: 'itm one harnesse for the kings Maiestie all graven and pcell guilte both for the felde and Tilte complete wʰ was commanded to be translated [altered] at the Kings goinge over to Bulloigne which lieth in peces parte translated and parte untranslated by A contrarie comaundement by the Kings Maiestie'. The mention of Boulogne is a reference to the invasion of France in 1544 (A. E. Dillon, 'Arms and Armour at Westminster, the Tower, and Greenwich 1547', *Archaeologia*, LI, pt.1, 1888, p.278). The gorget of a very similar armour in the Tower of London (No.II 8) is dated 1540. Claude Blair has suggested that the decoration of the Tower armour is by the Florentine, Giovanni de Maiano (*Connoisseur*, CXLIV, 1959, p.243).

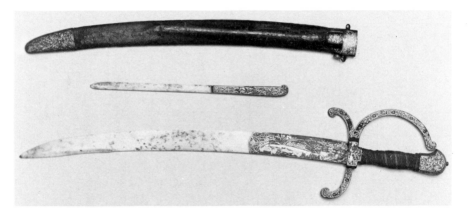

98 Woodknife and By-Knife of King Henry VIII (c.1545)

Of steel etched and gilt, the hilt is of iron and the grip (probably an eighteenth-century replacement) is of wood bound with iron wire. The sword is fitted with an eighteenth-century wooden scabbard covered with black leather to which are attached iron mounts from the original scabbard. The accompanying wood-knife is of steel and its handle is damascened in gold. Length of sword 654 mm (25¾ ins); length of by-knife 308 mm (12⅛ ins).

The etched decoration, originally on a blued ground which is now a russet colour, includes arabesques, scenes of boar hunts (on the quillons), the closing stages of the Siege of Boulogne in 1544 (on one face of the blade) and an elegiac inscription in Latin recording the capture of the town (on the other face of the blade).

The woodknife is probably one of the pair listed in the inventory of King Henry VIII's possessions drawn up in 1547 after his death, where they are described as two 'longe woodknives .... of Dego his making . . .'. Dego can be identified as the Spanish swordsmith and damascener, Diego de Çaias, who in 1542 was expelled from France where he had been working for the Dauphin, later Henri II. Probably by March 1543, certainly by October that year, he had entered King Henry VIII's service.

The history of the woodknife following the death of Henry VIII is not known. By 1798 it was in the possession of the gunmaker and antiquary, George Wallis. It then passed through the Londesborough, Spitzer and Odescalchi collections and finally, in the last decade, it has re-entered the Royal Collection (Claude Blair, 'A Royal Swordsmith and Damascener: Diego de Çaias', *Metropolitan Museum Journal*, vol.3, 1970, pp.149–198).

99 Medallion of King Henry VIII (3rd quarter of 16th century)

Of stone carved in relief with traces of gesso and pigment. Diameter of medallion (excluding frame) 37·7 cm (14⅞ ins). The carved oak frame, at one time gilded, is of a later date.

The figure of the King conforms to a type which derives from Holbein's painting on the wall of the Privy Chamber at Whitehall Palace (see No.81). Nothing is known of the early history of this relief.

Index of Names

Numbers shown are those in the catalogue

Concordance of Drawings

Parker	Cat. No.	Parker	Cat. No.
Frontispiece	88	39	46
1	3	42	54
2	2	43	72
3	1	44	52
4	10	45	63
5	11	46	74
6	7	47	43
7	8	48	70
8	9	49	49
9	16	50	67
10	12	51	68
11	17	53	66
12	14	54	51
13	15	55	76
14	30	56	64
15	31	57	53
16	35	58	44
17	32	59	77
18	33	60	20
19	62	61	19
22	40	63	48
23	34	64	79
24	56	65	80
25	59	66	26
26	21	67	69
27	61	68	78
29	36	69	27
30	57	70	73
31	29	72	45
32	38	73	47
33	42	75	65
34	55	78	60
35	39	79	24
36	41	80	75
37	18	81	71
38	23		